News & Literature House
Suppliers of
• Periodicals • Medical, Technical & General Books
44-45, Ist Floor, Kalawati Paliwal Market,
Gumanpura, Kota-7 (Raj.)
Phone : 0744-5121961 Mobile : 98290-38026
Fax : 0744-2392079 E-mail : nlh@kappa.net.in

Ashana Makhija - Kartika - 2013

The Indian classics are very old. They reflect the stream of thought and wisdom of India. The *Vedas* and the *Upanishads* are the oldest. The *Ramayana* and the *Mahabharata*, which have a central place in our lore, are read and sung in homes all over the country. The stories have held interest for the young and the old. They lay stress on values. Related by word of mouth thousands of times, generation after generation, they retain their freshness, charm and meaning. Their purport is at times direct, at times implied—the victory of virtue over evil, truth over falsehood, the sanctity of the pledged word, the triumph of love. Many characters are archetypes. They exalt and warn. Much more than moral-bearing, the classics have great literary excellence, and rich nuances of humour.

Tales from Indian Classics, in three volumes, present select stories to the children.

© by CBT 1990
Reprinted 1993, 1996, 1997, 1999, 2000, 2001,
2003 (twice), 2005, 2007, 2010, 2013.

ISBN 81-7011-467-5

All rights reserved. No part of this book may be reproduced in whole or in part, or stored in a retrieval system, or transmitted in any form or by any means, electronic, mechanical, photocopying, recording, or otherwise, without the prior written permission of the publisher.

Published by Children's Book Trust, Nehru House, 4 Bahadur Shah Zafar Marg, New Delhi-110002 and printed at its Indraprastha Press. Ph: 23316970-74
Fax: 23721090 e-mail: cbtnd@cbtnd.com Website: www.childrensbooktrust.com

TALES FROM INDIAN CLASSICS

Retold by Savitri
Illustrated by Pulak Biswas
and
Sukumar Chatterjee

Children's Book Trust, New Delhi

Ashana Makhija

CONTENTS

Ganapathi

Ganapathi was the son of Lord Shiva. He was a short, fat boy with an elephant's head. He was full of fun and frolic. He troubled people if they took no notice of him. He liked good food and wanted plenty to eat. Everyone tried to please him by offering him fruits, sweets, and other nice things to eat.

Kubera was the Lord of riches. He was so rich that nobody could say how much wealth he had. He was very proud of his wealth and thought he was greater than anyone else in the world. He wanted people to know how great he was.

He liked them to come begging for his help. Kings, nobles, and other important people went to him at one time or another seeking his help and he always helped them.

Kubera liked to spend his wealth in every possible way. He built big temples and huge palaces. He organised festivals. He arranged feasts. He gave rich gifts to rajas and noblemen. He helped the poor. But, with all his spending, his wealth only increased, and he had to find new ways of spending it. He thought long about this and decided to invite the gods themselves to big feasts. Lord Shiva was his favourite god. It was owing to Shiva's blessings that he

had become so rich. So Kubera wanted to invite Shiva and his family to a feast.

Kubera went to Kailash, offered his prayers to Shiva and said, "O Lord, I am grateful to you for all your blessings. I am now the richest in the world. I have helped the rich and the poor alike. Now everybody sings my praises."

"Well, well," said Shiva. "I have heard all this, but what brings you here now?"

"My Lord," said Kubera, "I have come here to invite you and your family and friends to a feast at my house. I shall call all the important people of the world. They all want to meet you to pay their respects."

Shiva smiled and said, "I am too old now. I don't like going out to eat."

"My Lord," cried Kubera, "you are breaking my heart. You can't do that to me, your beloved devotee. I came all the way here to invite you. If you feel you cannot come, may I invite Devi Parvati and the children?"

Shiva again smiled and said, "I don't think my wife would like to go out without me, and the children will not go without their mother."

Kubera was very disappointed. He fell at Shiva's feet and said, "My Lord, what will people think of me now? I told them that I was coming here to invite you. They all think that you never refuse anything I ask of you."

Shiva said, "I think I can help you in one way. I shall ask Ganapathi, my little son, to attend the feast."

Kubera agreed. He fixed a date for the feast and returned home.

Kubera made arrangements to hold the biggest feast ever held in the world. A huge dining hall was built and new kitchens were set up. Silver vessels and gold plates and dishes were specially made. Foodstuffs of all kinds were stored. He engaged hundreds of cooks and other servants.

Kubera invited many kings and their families, nobles and their friends, and all the other important people of the world.

As the day of the feast approached, guests began to arrive. Kings, queens, princes, and princesses came wearing colourful costumes and costly jewels. Kubera received them and put them up in splendid guest-houses. On the day of the feast, he and his family wore the finest clothes and the richest ornaments. They waited with the guests for the arrival of Ganapathi.

Ganapathi arrived at the appointed time. Kubera received him with respect and courtesy. He wanted to introduce him at once to the other guests, but Ganapathi said that he was very hungry and wanted his food first.

Kubera took Ganapathi to the dining hall, which was beautifully decorated. There were thousands of brightly lit lamps, and a sweet scent arose from sprinkled perfume and burnt incense. There was music, too. In the centre of the hall was spread a beautiful and very costly carpet. On one side of it were gold plates, and dishes filled with delicious food and fruits of many kinds.

Ganapathi sat down and started eating. He was very hungry and quickly ate up all the food that had been served. The plates were refilled and Ganapathi did not take long to empty them again. Once more all the plates and dishes were filled, and Ganapathi gobbled up all the food. More and yet more food was brought and it was eaten as soon as it was served.

Kubera ordered quicker service and people started run-

ning between the kitchen and the dining hall, bringing in more and more food and quickly removing the empty plates. Ganapathi was still so hungry that those who served could not keep pace with his eating. Soon he had eaten all the food prepared for thousands of people, and he was still asking for more.

Kubera ordered more food to be cooked. But Ganapathi stood up and said that he was so hungry he could not wait. Kubera prayed for time but Ganapathi was impatient. He went to the kitchen and ate all the food as it was being cooked. He went to the store-room and ate all the foodstuffs kept there. Still he was hungry. He came out and asked Kubera to give him something more to eat. Kubera was helpless.

Ganapathi went to Kubera's palace and ate up whatever food he could find there. He went to the rooms where Kubera kept his gold and ate that up. Still he was not satisfied. He turned to Kubera and said, "You wanted me to eat here. Give me some food or I shall have to eat you." Kubera took fright and started running. Ganapathi ran after him. Kubera ran faster and Ganapathi was just behind. They ran and ran for a long time until they reached Kailash. Kubera cried aloud to Shiva to come and save him. Shiva came out and Kubera fell at his feet.

"What is all this?" asked Shiva.

Ganapathi said, "Kubera did not give me enough to eat and I am still hungry."

"You go in and ask your mother to give you something," said Shiva, and Ganapathi left.

Shiva looked kindly at Kubera. Kubera begged to be forgiven for being too proud of his riches.

The House of Lac

The story of the 'Mahabharata' is about the Pandavas and the Kauravas.

The five Pandava brothers, Dharmaputra, Bhima, Arjuna, Nakula and Sahadeva, were the sons of Pandu, the King of Hastinapura. The Kauravas were the one hundred sons of Dhritarashtra, Pandu's elder brother. Dhritarashtra was blind. The people did not want a blind man to be their king. So Pandu was chosen king instead.

Pandu was a great ruler. He ruled the country well and the people loved him very much. But Pandu's rule did not last long. He died when his children were still young. So Dhritarashtra took charge of Pandu's children and acted as king till they grew up.

The Pandavas and the Kauravas lived in the same house and went to school together.

Even as children the Kauravas did not like the Pandavas. They knew that one day the Pandavas would take over the kingdom from Dhritarashtra. The Kauravas would then be no more than common people. They hated to think of themselves in such a position. They could not hope to become the rulers unless they could remove the Pandavas. So, from their young days the Kauravas had only one aim—to destroy the Pandavas.

As the Pandavas and the Kauravas grew older, their hatred and bitterness towards each other also grew. The Kauravas were jealous of the strength and beauty of the Pandava princes. There were many quarrels and fights between them. But the Pandavas always won. Duryodhana, the eldest of the Kauravas, hated the Pandavas most. Bhima was his chief rival and he hated Bhima more than anyone else.

At last the princes came of age. Dhritarashtra knew that he must now choose an heir to the throne. He longed to choose Duryodhana, his own eldest son, whom he loved very much. But he thought that would not be right, and he knew the people would not approve of it. So he decided to choose Dharmaputra, the eldest of the Pandavas, as king.

Duryodhana and his brothers were angry. They knew that the Pandavas had the right to the throne and that the people loved the Pandavas and were impatient at the delay in crowning Dharmaputra. Yet the Kauravas decided to prevent the Pandavas from getting the throne. They consulted their maternal uncle Sakuni. He was a most wicked man. He hated the Pandavas and wanted to help his nephews. The Kauravas and Sakuni went to the old king and pleaded that Duryodhana should be chosen king.

Duryodhana said, "Father, you are now the king. The king has the right to choose his successor. It is true the people want Dharmaputra to be the king. But they are fools. They do not know what they are saying. If Dharmaputra is made king, where shall we go? What will become of us and our children? We shall be like poor relations, dependent on the Pandavas even for food. It is far better to die than to be the slaves of the Pandavas."

"What you say is true," said Dhritarashtra. "But Dharmaputra is a good man. He loves everyone. He has a claim to the throne. The people know that and they will not forgive me if I make a wrong choice."

Duryodhana replied, "You have nothing to fear. The leaders of the army and all the elder statesmen are on our side. Send the Pandavas to some distant place for a while. When they are gone we can make our side stronger. We shall get the goodwill of the people and more people will be true to us. Send the Pandavas to Varanavata. Tell them the people of that place want them to go there."

The old king thought over the suggestion for a long time. In the end he agreed to carry out his son's wishes. He asked the Pandavas to go to Varanavata and stay there for some time.

The Pandavas felt that there was a hidden reason for sending them away. But they would not disobey Dhritarashtra. They agreed to go.

Duryodhana was happy that the Pandavas were going away. But he did not want them to come back. He talked to Sakuni and between them they formed a plan.

Duryodhana called his faithful servant, Purochana, and said, "The Pandavas are going to Varanavata. I want them all to die there. You must go immediately to Varanavata and build a palace for the Pandavas. The palace should be built of lac, wax, and other materials which will quickly go up in flames when it is set on fire. Cover the walls with plaster and get beautiful pictures painted on them. Spend any amount of money. Nobody must suspect anything. When the Pandavas reach there, you must stay with them. At a proper time, set fire to the building and see that not one of them escapes."

Purochana promised to do his best and left for Varanavata. He built a palace just as Duryodhana wanted. He then waited for the Pandavas to come.

The Pandavas and their mother, Kunti, left Hastinapura for Varanavata. Because the people loved them, they followed them, but the Pandavas told them to return to their homes. They promised to come back as soon as they could. On the way, Vidura, their wise uncle, warned them that there might be danger to their lives from fire. They must be careful.

The Pandavas arrived in Varanavata and the people there received them with great joy. Purochana met them and took them to the new palace. The Pandavas found it very beautiful, but they soon learnt that it was a fire trap. They pretended not to notice anything and began to live there. Shortly after, a messenger arrived from Vidura. He told the Pandavas that Vidura had sent him to help them. He said he would make a long underground tunnel from the palace to a safe place in a forest far away. If the palace

were set on fire, the Pandavas could escape through the tunnel. The Pandavas gladly accepted his suggestion. They worked day and night and the tunnel was ready in a few months.

The Pandavas spent their time hunting and merry-making. But always they knew there might be danger.

Purochana stayed in a room near the palace gate. He was on guard to see that the Pandavas did not escape. He was waiting for a good time to set fire to the palace.

Bhima, the strongest among the Pandavas, and Arjuna, the cleverest, were always alert, watching the movements of everyone who came near the palace. They were on the look-out for any visitor who might set it on fire.

A year passed and the Pandavas felt that Purochana would act soon. So they decided to act first. One night they themselves set fire to the palace and escaped through the tunnel. Purochana, caught unawares, was burnt to death. The whole building crumbled to ashes in no time.

The people of Varanavata thought that the Pandavas and their mother had died in the big fire. They were filled with grief at losing their beloved princes.

News reached Hastinapura that the Pandavas had been burnt to death by accident in a fire. Old king Dhritarashtra suffered great sorrow. The Kauravas were very happy, but pretended they were grieved.

The Pandavas and their mother reached the forest through the tunnel. They decided to travel in disguise until they got back to Hastinapura.

Bhima and Hanuman

The Pandavas and the Kauravas lived in peace for some time. But the Kauravas were still jealous of the Pandavas and wanted to grab the whole kingdom. They invited the Pandavas to a game of dice and the Pandavas accepted the invitation. Sakuni cheated the Pandavas by using loaded dice. The Kauravas won the game. The Pandavas lost their kingdom and everything else they had. Also, they had to leave their country and live in the forest for twelve years.

Life in the jungle was hard, but Draupadi looked after their comforts and the Pandavas lived happily.

One day a gentle breeze blew over the forest bringing the scent of an uncommon flower. Draupadi liked the scent very much. She wanted to have some of these flowers. But who would get them for her?

She knew that only Bhima could get the flowers. She asked him to go and get them for her. But Bhima did not want to waste his time hunting for flowers. He said he did not know where the flowers grew. Draupadi was in tears and said, "If you cannot get the flowers for me, who else will get them? You do not love me. Forget that I asked you for them."

Bhima could not bear to see Draupadi in tears. So he promised he would go and get the flowers.

The next day, Bhima was on his way searching for the flowers. Nobody could tell him where they grew, but Bhima knew he should go in the direction from which the wind blew. It was the wind that had carried the sweet scent of the flowers to Draupadi.

Bhima had to pass through a thick forest. There was no path and he had to make his way forward by cutting down trees and breaking up rocks with his heavy club. His journey through the forest made such a lot of noise that even the wild animals were frightened and ran away.

On his way Bhima had to pass through a beautiful garden. In it grew flowers of all colours and many fruit trees. There was a path through the garden and Bhima followed it. Suddenly he saw an old monkey lying on the ground right across his path. He was angry that a monkey should block his path. He felt insulted.

He stopped and said, "You old monkey, how dare you block my path? Get up and move to one side so that I can go on."

The monkey lay still as if he had not heard Bhima. "Didn't you hear me?" cried Bhima. "Get out of my way before I smash your silly head."

The monkey slowly opened his eyes. He looked at Bhima and said, "I am too old and I have no strength left in me to move. Why don't you walk round me and leave me alone?"

"You old monkey," said Bhima, "do you know to whom you are speaking? Haven't you heard of Bhima, the mighty, the great Pandava? I am he. I always walk a straight path. I don't allow anyone to stand in my way. I

never admit defeat."

The monkey said, "I am very old and sick. But your big talk makes me laugh. You say you never admit defeat. What happened to you when the Kauravas drove you out of your home? And now you are living in the jungle like wild animals."

"Stop talking nonsense!" shouted Bhima. "You are a silly monkey that jumps from tree to tree. How can you understand the strong Bhima? Perhaps you have not heard how Bhima fought and won so many battles, and killed ogres and giants."

"A strong man!" sneered the monkey. "Where was your strength when Dussasan insulted your wife? You stood there like a lump of stone when he touched her. Was your courage away on a pilgrimage then?"

Bhima said, "I wish a strong man were talking to me instead of you. Then I could show him my strength. People would only laugh at me if they heard that Bhima had killed an old monkey."

Then the monkey said, "A big man like you should not quarrel with a sick, old monkey. You can easily jump over me and go on your way. Or if you don't like that, you can move my tail to one side and then go. If you don't like to touch my dirty tail, why don't you push it aside with your club?"

"Suppose your tail snaps in two?" asked Bhima.

"Suppose your club breaks?" replied the monkey.

Bhima was very annoyed with the monkey. But he was getting late. He decided to push the monkey's tail aside with his club.

He put his big club below the tail and tried to raise it. The tail did not move. He tried again but still it would not move. Bhima used more strength but the tail was still where it was. Then he used all his strength. He heaved with all his might, but still he could not move it even one inch. He tried again and again and failed every time. Bhima thought he would take the club away from that part of the tail and use it at another part. But the club would not come out. It was stuck under the tail. Bhima pulled it once, he pulled it twice, he pulled it a hundred times. But he could not pull it out. He grew tired, but he could not leave his club there. He looked at the old monkey. The monkey lay there, calmly smiling.

Bhima wondered how such a small, old monkey could be equal to his own great strength. What would people say if they heard that Bhima had been defeated by a monkey? Perhaps, Bhima thought, the monkey possessed some magic powers, or perhaps it was a devil who was taking this form to get the better of him. But he was not the man to be afraid of magic or the devil.

He cried, "You silly monkey, who are you? You are not a monkey. No monkey ever had such strength as you have. You have got magic powers or else you are a devil. I shall show you how I can deal with you. I challenge you to a duel."

"I am not a devil, nor have I any magic powers," replied the monkey. "I am Hanuman, the servant of the great Sri Rama who killed Ravana." As he spoke the old monkey grew and grew into the huge form of Hanuman.

Bhima was astonished but happy to meet Hanuman. He touched Hanuman's feet and asked to be forgiven. Hanuman embraced him lovingly and said, "I have been wanting to meet you for a long time. I saw you coming. I blocked your path just so that I could talk to you. The rest was all fun. I am sure you must be on your way to do something very important. You are late. Go quickly, I must not delay you further. By the way, what is it you are out to do?"

Bhima told him the reason for his journey. Then Hanuman said, "So you are not going to kill another giant or fight a battle. You are only going to pick flowers for your wife! A big adventure for the great Bhima! Go, I will not keep you back any more. But do you know where those flowers grow?"

Bhima then asked Hanuman to help him find the flowers, and Hanuman told him where they grew and how he could reach the place.

Bhima took leave of Hanuman and continued on his journey. The flowers grew in a large lake in a beautiful garden. Many other flowers were growing there, too. The garden belonged to Kubera, the Lord of wealth. He had an army there to guard the flowers. And in the lake he kept

hundreds of fierce crocodiles, which killed anyone who entered the water.

Bhima reached Kubera's garden. The guards would not allow him to enter. They attacked him. Bhima fought them. He chased them with his club. They were afraid of him and they all ran away.

Then Bhima went to the lake. The crocodiles rushed to attack him. But Bhima raised his club and hit out at the crocodiles. They all swam away. Now Bhima was able to enter the water and pick the flowers that Draupadi wanted. He collected as many flowers as he could carry. He then turned to go back. As he reached the shore he found that the guards had come back with many more men. They were all eager to fight him. Bhima held the flowers carefully in one hand. With the other hand he fought the guards with his club. And he again drove them all away.

Bhima returned home. He gave Draupadi the flowers that she had longed for. Draupadi was very happy to receive those rare flowers.

Cousins and Enemies

The Pandavas lived in the forest for a long time. It was difficult and dangerous to live there. The Kauravas believed that all the Pandavas would die in the forest. But the Pandavas did not die, and the twelve years they had to spend there were now coming to an end. The Kauravas did not want them to come back and claim their kingdom. They wanted to know how the Pandavas were getting on. They sent a spy to find out.

The spy returned and reported that the Pandavas were quite well and were living happily. This made the Kauravas angry. Duryodhana was so angry that he kicked the man who brought the news.

The Kauravas discussed among themselves to decide what action they should take. Duryodhana suggested that they could frighten the Pandavas by taking a military parade into the forest. That would show them how strong the Kauravas were. The Pandavas would then be afraid to come back. Everyone liked the idea.

Soon orders were issued to organize the biggest military parade the world had ever seen. Duryodhana himself looked after all the arrangements. Within a few days everything was ready.

One morning the parade started. It was led by the Kauravas in their beautiful chariots. They were followed by many elephants, hundreds of horses, and thousands of soldiers, all armed and ready for battle.

People from far and near went to see the greatest parade they had ever seen. After passing through cities and villages the procession reached the forest. The birds and animals all fled away, frightened by the noise made by the marching army. The parade reached the part of the forest where the Pandavas had their camp.

The procession stopped by the side of a river and a camp was set up there. The forest around was beautiful. There were trees with lovely flowers and sweet fruits. The river was full and the water was as clear as crystal. The Kauravas felt jealous that the Pandavas were staying in such a beautiful place. The wicked Sakuni thought of a way to harm the Pandavas. He suggested that the water of the river should be poisoned so that when the Pandavas drank it they would die or fall ill. The Kauravas liked the idea and at once went and poured poison into the river water.

At that time, Chitrasena, a powerful Gandharva, was staying in the same forest. He was told that some people were poisoning the water of the river. He was very angry and rushed to the Kauravas' camp with his followers. He recognized them and said, "I know who you are. You are poisoning the water of the river in order to kill the Pandavas. I am going to teach you a lesson."

Duryodhana shouted, "Do you know who we are? If you want to live, stop talking and surrender to us. You must be our slaves. Otherwise we shall kill you all with our great army." With these words he ordered his men to fight the Gandharvas.

A terrible battle followed. The Kauravas fought with great strength and courage. But the Gandharvas were stronger. Many elephants, horses, and men of the Kaurava army were killed and the rest of them fled. The Kauravas were captured. Chitrasena said, "We are going to take you to our country and you shall be put to work as slaves." The Gandharvas tied the Kauravas to their chariots and started the journey home.

The Kauravas had no way of escape. They knew the Pandavas were somewhere near. They called loudly to the Pandavas to come to their rescue.

The Pandavas heard them. Dharmaputra said to his brothers, "I hear the Kauravas calling to us for help. I do not know what has happened to them, but they must be in danger. Go and help them."

Bhima, the strongest of the Pandavas, said, "I know what has happened to the Kauravas. They came to the forest to harm us. They had a fight with Chitrasena and his followers. Then the Kauravas were defeated and taken prisoners, and now they are being marched to Chitrasena's home to work as slaves. The Kauravas are our enemies and their one aim in life is to destroy us. Why should we go and help them? Let them be taken as slaves by Chitrasena."

"Yes, they are indeed our enemies," said Dharmaputra. "But they are our cousins and they are in danger. They are seeking our help, and we have to help them. Go and set them free."

Arjuna said he would go and do his duty as ordered by Dharmaputra. Bhima could not stay behind. So Bhima and Arjuna went to the help of the Kauravas.

They met Chitrasena and told him that he would have

to set free the Kauravas. Chitrasena was surprised that the Pandavas had come to help the Kauravas, though they were their enemies.

Chitrasena was a friend of the Pandavas and he did not want to fight with them. So he set free all the Kauravas and told them to go home. He told the Pandavas that he was very happy to see how noble they had been in coming to the help of their enemies.

The Kauravas returned home in great shame.

Draupadi Swayamwara

The Pandavas were living in Ekachakra when they heard about princess Draupadi. She was the daughter of Drupada, the King of Panchala. She was the most beautiful princess of the time. She was also talented and very noble. The kings and princes of many countries desired to marry her.

King Drupada had hoped that Draupadi would marry Arjuna, the cleverest and the most handsome of the Pandavas. But he heard, with great sorrow, of the tragic death of the Pandavas at Varanavata. Now he had to find some other suitable husband for Draupadi. There were many suitors, young princes of great name, seeking her hand. But King Drupada could not choose among them so he decided to hold a swayamwara for his daughter.

A swayamwara was a kind of marriage in which a princess could choose her husband from among a number of suitors. The suitors would be introduced to the princess one by one and she would make her own choice. Sometimes the suitors were asked to perform some difficult deed of strength or skill, and he who did it first would marry the princess.

A day was fixed for Draupadi's swayamwara and invitations were sent to many kings and princes. They were all eager to go.

The Pandavas, still in disguise, decided to attend Draupadi's swayamwara. They all went to the capital of Panchala, taking Kunti with them. There they stayed in the house of a potter.

On the day of the swayamwara, the Pandavas left Kunti at the potter's house and went to the palace. They went there not as princes but as brahmins and took their seats among the visitors.

The kings and princes had arrived. Each one hoped to win the hand of Draupadi. There were famous soldiers among them. The Kauravas, confident of winning the princess, were also there.

The large marriage hall was beautifully decorated. The guests took their seats. King Drupada and his son escorted Draupadi to the hall. Everyone stood up. All looked eagerly at the most beautiful princess they had ever seen.

King Drupada declared that Draupadi would marry any man of noble birth who could string the bow that was in the hall and shoot at the target. The bow was huge and heavy. The target was a little metal fish hung very high above the ground. Below it was a disc that kept turning round and round. The disc had holes in it. A vessel of water was placed on the ground below the target and the suitor had to shoot at the fish by looking at its image in the water. The arrow had to pass through one of the holes in the disc. It was an almost impossible task. But the kings and princes were eager to compete, for each wanted to win Draupadi. One by one they got up and went to the mighty bow to try their luck. Many could not lift it. Some could lift it but were unable to string it. The most famous among

them were able to lift the bow and string it but failed to shoot the fish.

King Drupada felt very sad. The kings and princes looked at each other. They felt ashamed that no one could shoot the fish. Many said it was an impossible task.

Then Arjuna stood up from among the crowd of brahmins, and walked towards the bow. Everybody looked at him in surprise. They wondered how a brahmin dared to try to do something that kings and princes could not do. But Arjuna boldly went and picked up the bow and strung it. He then shot five arrows, one after the other, at the target. The fish fell to the ground. There was great joy among the crowd. Draupadi looked at the splendid youth and put her garland round his neck.

Some of the kings and princes said that it was not right that a brahmin should win the hand of a princess. They wanted to start a fight, but others declared that the princess had been won fairly.

Arjuna and his brothers went back to the potter's house to tell their mother the happy news. It was night when they reached the house. Arjuna knocked at the door and shouted to Kunti, "Mother, I have won a wonderful prize."

"Share it with all your brothers," Kunti replied.

She came out, and then realised what the prize was. "My sons," said Kunti, "I cannot take back what I have once said. Draupadi must be wife to you all." So Draupadi became the wife of the five brothers.

King Drupada was not happy at the swayamwara. He did not know who the young man was. Was he really a brahmin? Or was he somebody who was disguised as a

brahmin? He wanted to find out. He sent a spy to the potter's house. The spy returned and informed the king that the Pandavas were not dead. It was Arjuna who had won the hand of Draupadi. Drupada was filled with joy. He sent messengers to invite the Pandavas to the palace but he did not tell them that he knew their secret. When they arrived wearing the clothes of simple sadhus, the king received them with great honour. He asked them to tell him who they really were. Dharmaputra then told Drupada the whole story.

Drupada and all the people were filled with joy when

they learnt that it was Arjuna who had won the hand of Draupadi. So the marriage of Draupadi to the Pandavas was celebrated with great joy.

The Kauravas heard the news that the Pandavas were still alive. They were sorry to hear that the Pandavas did not die in the fire. Vidura, Bhishma, Drona, and other respected elders, advised King Dhritarashtra to ask the Pandavas to return home. The Pandavas and the Kauravas then made peace between themselves. They divided the country into two parts, one half to be ruled by the Pandavas and the other by the Kauravas.

The Pandavas set up their capital at Indraprastha. The Kauravas had their capital at Hastinapura.

Bakasura

The Pandavas and their mother, Kunti, wandered about the country in disguise. After some time they reached a settlement, Ekachakra. There they stayed in a brahmin's house. The brahmin and his wife treated them kindly.

Kunti discovered that the brahmin and his wife were in deep sorrow. She wanted to find out what the trouble was, and so she asked the brahmin's wife about it.

"There is nothing we can tell you," was the answer.

"But," Kunti said, "I see that great grief is eating your heart. Tell me what is the matter."

The woman said, "We have our own sorrow. It is not proper to tell guests about it."

"Please tell me what it is so that I may share your sorrow with you," said Kunti.

"No, you are our honoured guest. We must not make you feel unhappy," the brahmin's wife replied.

"If you will not tell me what it is, we shall go away from here and stay somewhere else," Kunti answered.

The brahmin's wife sat silent for a time. Then with tears in her eyes she began to tell the story of their grief.

"Beyond the mountains, some miles away, lives a fierce giant in a big cave. His name is Baka, or Bakasura, as people call him. He used to come down to the villages and take away men, women, and cattle and eat them up.

"Our king tried to fight the giant with a big army. But Bakasura is very strong. He defeated the king and his army. The king fled to save his life, so the people had to face the giant. We decided to make peace with him. Bakasura agreed not to come down from the mountain if we sent him a cart-load of cooked food, two bullocks, and a human being daily. So these are sent every day. The bullocks and the human being carry the cooked food. Bakasura eats the food, the bullocks, and the human being as well. We have kept our promise.

"Every day one person is chosen by lot and sent with the cart-load of food. Our turn has now come. Tomorrow our family has to send a man with Bakasura's food. We are a small family; my husband, myself, and our only son. We do not know who should go. Each one of us would like to go for the sake of the other two." As she ended her story the brahmin's wife burst into tears.

Kunti tried to comfort her. She said, "You have only one son, but I have five. I shall send one of my sons instead of one of you."

"Oh, no, no," cried the poor woman. "You are our guests and we shall never allow our guests to suffer for us. We shall send our own son and bear the sorrow."

Kunti only smiled in reply. She called all her sons to her and told them of the danger facing the brahmin's family. "I think you, Bhima, can take the food to the giant tomorrow morning," she said.

"I?" said Bhima. "Don't you like me, mother, that you send me to be killed by the giant?"

The brahmin woman protested. She said she would not

allow any of Kunti's children to be killed. Bhima laughed and told her that he was only joking.

"As a matter of fact," he said, "I want to go and see this giant myself. You know I am a strong man. I shall meet the giant and I shall return."

It took a long time for Kunti to make the brahmin and his wife believe that Bhima would defeat the giant if he were allowed to go. At last they agreed.

Early the next morning Bhima set out, riding in a cart filled with food and driven by two fat bullocks. It was a long way to the mountain, but Bhima was in no hurry. When he reached the mountain, the giant was shouting. He was very angry because the food was late.

Bhima stopped some distance away from the giant. He unyoked the bullocks and then quietly unpacked the bundles of food. He sat down and began to eat what he had brought for the giant.

The giant roared in anger. Bhima told him that he was only making the giant's work easier. The giant could eat

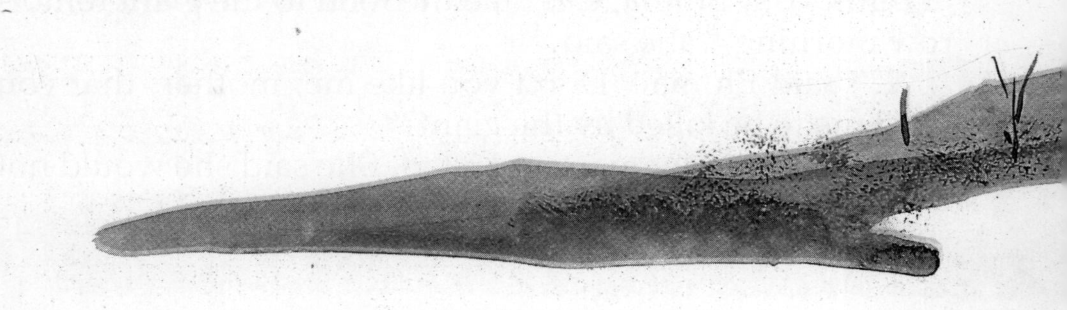

him with all the food inside.

Bakasura now became even more angry. He took a huge rock and ran towards Bhima to crush him to death. Bhima pulled up a tree to use as a club. When the giant came near, Bhima hit him with the tree.

A big battle began. Bhima fought with the giant, giving blow for blow. At last he killed the giant. The giant lay like a huge hill.

Bhima returned to Ekachakra in the evening. All the people gathered to thank him for saving their lives from Bakasura.

Bhasmasura

Bhasmasura was a wicked and greedy person. He wanted to be a powerful king. But he was neither strong nor brave. He knew he could not wage wars or defeat other kings.

Bhasmasura, therefore, wished to obtain some magic powers. He decided to worship Lord Shiva and ask for such powers.

Bhasmasura went to a dense jungle. There, he selected a quiet place under a huge tree and settled down to worship Shiva. His prayer lasted a long time.

At last, Lord Shiva appeared before Bhasmasura and said, "I am greatly pleased with you. What can I do for you?"

"O Lord," said Bhasmasura, "I only want your blessings. There is no other purpose behind my devotion to you."

Shiva said, "You have my blessings. But you would surely like to receive something from me as a gift. It is yours for the asking."

"Then, my Lord," said Bhasmasura, "let me have the power that I ask for. By that power, anybody whose head I touch with my right hand should be reduced to ashes."

"I hereby grant you that power," replied Shiva. "Anybody whose head you touch with your right hand will die and be reduced to ashes."

Bhasmasura laughed. He was happy with the magic power he had received from Shiva.

"My Lord," said Bhasmasura, "you must now allow me to test the power you have given me."

Bhasmasura jumped up to touch the head of Lord Shiva.

Shiva was in danger. He knew he would be reduced to ashes, if he allowed Bhasmasura to touch his head. So Shiva ran for his life.

Bhasmasura ran after Shiva.

Shiva ran quickly over hills and mountains, crossed rivers and passed through thick jungles. But Bhasmasura was close behind him, with his right hand raised ready to touch Shiva and reduce him to ashes.

Shiva needed help. He knew that unless somebody came to his help, Bhasmasura would kill him. Shiva, therefore, prayed to Lord Vishnu to save his life.

Vishnu heard Shiva's prayer and appeared before him.

"You just hide here for some time," Vishnu told Shiva. "I shall deal with Bhasmasura."

In a second, Lord Vishnu changed his form. He became Mohini, the most beautiful of women.

Bhasmasura, running after Shiva, stopped at the sight of Mohini. He asked her, "Did you see Shiva running this way? He was just in front of me. But then he somehow suddenly disappeared. Where did he go?"

Mohini fixed her lovely eyes on Bhasmasura and said, "My Lord, you look very tired. Take a little rest before you start chasing Shiva again. Sit here in the cool shade. I shall fan you. Then you will feel better."

Bhasmasura looked at Mohini. She was so beautiful that he fell in love with her immediately.

"Who are you?" he asked. "How did you come here?"

She replied coyly, "I am Mohini. I live in this jungle with my parents. We always help those who pass this way. You look hungry. Can I go and bring you some fruits?"

"No, don't go away from me," replied Bhasmasura. "Your presence is the best food for me." Then he added, "I love you, Mohini. Will you marry me?"

"How can I marry you?" asked Mohini. "You may have a number of wives already."

"You are wrong, Mohini," said Bhasmasura. "I have no wife. You will be my only wife."

"Yes, I shall be your only wife now," said Mohini, "but you may have other wives later. How can I trust you?"

"I give you my word," replied Bhasmasura. "I will not look at any other woman if you marry me."

"Men always say so," laughed Mohini, "I have no faith in them."

Bhasmasura said, "You mistake me, Mohini. I tell you that I will not take another wife, if you marry me."

"All right," said Mohini, "then please swear that you will not take another wife."

"I swear that I will not take another wife if you marry me," said Bhasmasura.

"That is not swearing," said Mohini. "Take the solemn oath, touching your head with your right hand. Then I shall trust you."

"Of course I shall take the solemn oath," said Bhasmasura. "I want you to trust me."

Bhasmasura rose up and touched his head with his right hand.

The moment Bhasmasura touched his head, he was reduced to ashes. Bhasmasura was no more.

Shiva came out of his hiding place and looked at Mohini. He was grateful to her and embraced her.

In a flash, Mohini vanished, smiling at Shiva, and in her place stood Lord Vishnu.

Vali and Ravana

Ravana, the king of Lanka, was at the height of his glory. He had fought and defeated many kings. He lived a life of luxury. But there was Indra who lived in greater luxury. Ravana was jealous of Indra and he waited for a chance to wage war against him.

One day, Ravana called his son, Meghanath, to his side and said, "Meghanath, you are a great soldier. Your fame has spread all over the world. But, lately, you have been idle. It is time you showed your strength again to the world and its people."

Ravana added, "You know, I have defeated all my enemies. But there is Indra who does not like me. We have to teach him a lesson. Why not go and fight him? We are sure to win."

Meghanath liked the idea. He made all the arrangements for a war with Indra. Soon, father and son marched out of Lanka with a huge army.

Ravana and Meghanath reached the gates of Indra's palace. They challenged Indra to come out and fight. Indra had no choice. He accepted the challenge.

Indra, too, had a big army. A terrible battle took place. Finally, Indra and his forces were defeated.

Indra was taken prisoner and Meghanath marched him off to Lanka. Ravana and his troops looted Indra's palace and returned home in triumph.

Back in Lanka, Ravana chained Indra to a tall pillar. Indra became an object of fun and ridicule for the people at Ravana's palace.

For many days, Indra remained a prisoner. He was unable to escape. Then he started praying to all the other gods to come to his help. Lord Vishnu, the god of gods, heard his prayers and requested Brahma to help Indra.

Brahma went to Lanka. Ravana received him with great respect. "Look, Ravana," said Brahma, "I hear that you have kept Indra here as a prisoner, chained to a pillar. You don't realise what you have done. It is a shame that you should do such a thing. Release Indra immediately and ask his pardon."

Now, Brahma was one of the few gods whom Ravana respected. So Ravana did not wish to displease Brahma. Indra was immediately set free.

Ravana ordered a grand festival in Lanka to celebrate his victory. There were big processions. A durbar was held and Meghanath was given the title of 'Indrajit' because of his victory over Indra.

While these celebrations were going on, Narada visited Lanka. Ravana received him with great courtesy and respect. "I have come to greet you in your big victory," said Narada to Ravana.

Ravana was pleased. He said, "Oh, you also have heard of it. It was really a great victory. Indra was defeated and taken prisoner. Meghanath brought him here and chained him to a pillar, like a monkey. You ought to have come a little earlier. Then you would have seen Indra chained to the pillar."

Ravana added, "But unfortunately I could not keep him long because poor Brahma took pity on him. In fact, Brahma came to see me. With tears in his eyes, he begged me to release Indra. You know, Brahma has great respect for me and I had to oblige him. And so I let Indra go."

"All the world is singing your praise," said Narada, "except someone whom I met on the way."

"Who is that?" roared Ravana.

"Oh, it is only a monkey," replied Narada. "But it is a big monkey—Vali, the monkey king. I don't wish to tell you all that he told me about you. In fact, I am afraid to tell you."

Ravana was angry. He said to Narada, "O great sage, tell me everything. What did this monkey say about me?"

Narada smiled. He said, "I will tell you all, if you insist. This monkey, Vali, feels that you, the great Ravana, are no match for him, that you know it, and that is why you dare not face him. I think that monkey should be taught a lesson. It is dangerous to keep him free. He must be beaten. His bones must be broken. He must be chained, and brought here for the children to play with."

Ravana was furious. He called his son and ordered him to get ready with the army. Narada laughed.

"It is a shame for you to fight a mere monkey with an army," said Narada. "The whole world will laugh at you, if you take an army to fight a monkey. It is a pity you don't know your own strength. To deal with a monkey, there is no need for an army or weapons. You can deal with him yourself. If you like, I shall come with you."

Ravana thought for a moment and agreed to go with Narada. They set out immediately and reached the place where Vali was living.

"Look," said Narada, "there is Vali."

"Where is he?" asked Ravana. "I see only a hill. Is he beyond the hill?"

Narada replied, "No, no, that is not a hill. It is Vali himself. Remember, I told you he was big. But don't be afraid of him. He is only a monkey. When he sees you, he is sure to jump up and climb some tall tree. You must catch him before that. See his tail? Why not catch hold of him by the tail, so that he can't run away?"

Ravana looked at Vali from head to foot. He was frightened. Vali was such a huge monkey.

"He seems to be at prayer," Ravana told Narada. "Let us wait a little, until he has finished his prayers. Then I shall deal with him."

Narada said, "Your words are very fine. But they are not the words of Ravana, the great and mighty Lord of Lanka. Tell me, O Ravana, are you afraid of Vali, a mere monkey? It is true that Vali is at prayer, but that is the best time to catch him."

Ravana went forward. But he stopped when Vali's huge tail moved a little.

Narada looked at Ravana and smiled at him with scorn.

Ravana saw that. Quickly, he went forward again and caught hold of Vali's tail with one hand.

Vali's tail moved a little, formed a loop, and tied up Ravana's arm in a knot. Ravana could not draw his hand back. He looked at Narada for advice.

Narada said, "Use the other hand, Ravana, and pull that monkey's tail quickly."

Ravana tried that and the other hand was also caught in Vali's long tail.

In a moment, the tail moved round and round over Ravana's body. Ravana found himself completely bound and helpless. He lay like a bundle, tied to Vali's tail.

Narada went to Ravana and said, "O great and mighty King Ravana, I have to go now. Please don't be upset. I shall go and tell your great son, who defeated Indra, to come and help you out."

Narada went on his way, without even looking back at the helpless Ravana.

Vali finished his prayers and stood up. He did not take any notice of Ravana, who was still tied to his tail.

Vali set out on a pilgrimage. He jumped over mountains and crossed seas and oceans. He bathed in many sacred rivers. Ravana remained firmly tied to his tail all the time.

Vali held a grand durbar after his return from the pilgri-

mage. All the monkeys of the world attended the durbar to pay their homage to Vali. During the durbar, someone noticed something strange on Vali's tail. The monkeys gathered round it. They saw that it was a large man tied to Vali's tail.

The monkeys were amused. They teased Ravana.

Then Vali turned round to see what was going on. He saw Ravana tied to his tail.

Vali immediately released Ravana. He asked Ravana how he came to be there and how long he had been there.

Ravana looked very miserable. With his head bowed, he told Vali the whole story. He said he was sorry for having come to fight Vali.

Vali was kind to Ravana. He said he was sorry for all that had happened. He requested Ravana to go back home.

Vali said to Ravana, "Please don't have any illfeeling towards me. And please don't be jealous of people or of the gods."

Ravana went home, sad and ashamed of himself. But he was a wiser man after this adventure.

Kaliyan

Krishna was the most lovely child in the world. He was dark and handsome. He wore pretty clothes and beautiful ornaments. His hair was tied in a knot on the top of his head. There was always a peacock feather in it. Little Krishna was the darling of all the people.

Krishna's childhood was full of fun and frolic. He had many friends. He went about the village and played with his friends. He was their leader. He led them into many adventures. He liked to play tricks on people, or make fun of them. His parents were sometimes annoyed at his pranks. But everybody liked him.

Krishna became a cowherd. He liked the cows and calves and the green fields in which they grazed. All the cowherds were his friends. Together they used to take the cattle out to the jungle in the morning and bring them back home in the evening. In the jungle there was plenty of grass and water for the cattle. The jungle was also an ideal place where Krishna and his friends could play and make merry.

Krishna was fond of music. He could play very well on the flute. His music delighted all who heard it. In the jungle Krishna would sit on the branch of a tree, or on a

big rock and play his flute. The cowherds would sit on the grass and listen to the music. The cows and calves, too, would stop grazing and go near Krishna to hear his sweet music. Even the wild animals in the jungle became tame at the sound of Krishna's flute.

At home, too, Krishna's music attracted people. Whenever he played the flute, men, women, and children stopped their work and ran to him. Krishna was loved by all.

Once, a huge snake named Kaliyan came to live in the river Yamuna. It was to this river that the cows and cowherds went to drink.

Kaliyan was a very poisonous snake. Soon, the river water became poisonous. Whoever drank the water from the Yamuna fell dead. All the fish in the river died because of the poison and began to float in the water. Crocodiles ran away from the poisoned water to the river bank. There, they attacked the animals and damaged the crops. Even the trees on the river banks dried up. Kaliyan became the deadly enemy of the land and the people.

Krishna heard of the poisonous snake. All the people were complaining about Kaliyan. But everybody feared Kaliyan. Little Krishna decided that he would punish Kaliyan for his wickedness.

One day, Krishna went alone to the Yamuna in search of the big snake. He found that Kaliyan lived in the deepest part of the river. Krishna jumped into the river and swam to Kaliyan's home.

Kaliyan was annoyed at the little dark boy who tried to disturb him. He rushed at Krishna to kill him with one stroke. But Krishna quickly moved up to the surface of the water. Kaliyan followed him.

In a flash, Krishna got hold of Kaliyan's huge head and stood on it. Krishna did not give the big snake a chance to bite him.

Kaliyan tried to shake him off, but Krishna stayed on his head. Kaliyan tried to twist himself round Krishna and squeeze him to death. But Krishna proved too strong for the snake.

Kaliyan then dived deep into the water. He wanted to drown Krishna. But Krishna was able to stay without breathing for as long as he wanted. Kaliyan was forced to come up for a breath of air.

Kaliyan was angry but helpless. Krishna stayed on Kaliyan's head. Then Krishna started kicking and stamping. Kaliyan struggled hard to throw Krishna off.

With both hands Krishna held the two sides of the snake's big head and kicked him as hard as he could.

Hundreds of frightened people gathered on the banks of the Yamuna. But Krishna seemed to be dancing happily on the deadly snake's head.

Slowly, Kaliyan began to lose strength. He was unable

to bear the pain of Krishna's attack.

Kaliyan started vomiting poison, and Krishna continued to kick him until all the poison came out.

Kaliyan gave up the struggle. He knew his end was near. His only hope now was to seek Krishna's mercy.

Kaliyan prayed to Krishna, He begged Krishna to spare his life. He promised to do whatever Krishna wanted him to do.

Krishna heard the prayer. He released Kaliyan from his grip. He ordered Kaliyan to go far away, and not come back to the Yamuna.

Kaliyan bowed his head. He quietly left the Yamuna.

The people cheered Krishna as he swam ashore.

Satya's Marriage

Satya was the most beautiful and most gifted girl in the world. She was a princess—the daughter of the rich and powerful King of Kosala. Her fame spread far and wide. Many royal princes asked the King of Kosala for her hand in marriage.

Satya reached the age of marriage and the king had to find a suitable match for her. Every one of the princes who wished to marry Satya was great in his own way. The king therefore found it difficult to choose one. He thought over the matter for many days and decided to hold a contest.

The king announced that any prince who could yoke the seven wild bulls he kept in his stables would win the hand of Satya in marriage.

A day was fixed for the marriage. Invitations were sent to all the suitable kings and princes to come and try their luck and their skill in the contest. The king also made all arrangements to celebrate the marriage in grand style.

New palaces were built for the royal guests. Large kitchens and huge dining halls were put up, and big feasts arranged. Famous musicians and dancers were invited to entertain the guests. The city was decorated and lit up.

The guests started arriving. Every king and every prince

hoped that he would win the contest and marry Satya. Every one of them came in a large procession. In every procession there were elephants, chariots, horses, palanquins, and soldiers. The kings and princes also brought their ministers and court officials, and many servants carrying boxes of jewels and clothes.

All the guests were received with great honour. They were housed in beautiful palaces. They were feasted and entertained most splendidly.

On the marriage day, the royal guests set out in their best clothes and jewels. They assembled on one side of a large field which was fenced on all sides. The King of Kosala arrived with his family, his ministers, court officials, and friends. He told the big gathering that his daughter, Satya, would marry the first prince who could yoke the seven wild bulls together. He then ordered the contest to begin.

The ceremony began with the beating of drums and the sounding of bugles. The pipers and trumpeters joined in. The music was exciting.

Seven large cages were then brought in. The attendants opened the doors of the cages. Seven huge, fierce-looking bulls rushed out. They moved about, challenging everyone.

Every prince desired to win Satya and wanted to get in first to try his luck. Many of them rushed in together, in the hope of yoking the wild bulls.

One king, who had won many battles and thought he was the strongest man to enter the contest, walked boldly towards one of the wild bulls. The bull charged at him with great force. He was tossed, and he fell to the ground. The bull followed him but the brave man got up and ran for his life.

A prince, one who had killed many wild animals, rushed at one of the bulls. The bull gored him and he fell down unconscious. Another prince approached a bull. But he then felt frightened and ran out of the field. One prince who tried to catch one of the bulls was kicked by the animal. He withdrew with a broken leg.

Everybody laughed when one of the kings caught the tail of a bull and the bull ran up and down, with the king dangling on its tail.

A prince tried to catch a bull by the horns; and soon he was seen flying through the air. The bulls trampled on one of the kings. Another king lost an eye; yet another lost an arm.

All the kings and princes tried their best. But none of them was able to catch the bulls and yoke them together.

Everybody was upset. Some of the princes said that the King of Kosala had set an impossible task for them. They said that the king must choose one of them to marry his daughter. They argued that the marriage had been fixed and it must take place.

The King of Kosala was very sad that the contest had failed. He ordered the bulls to be put back in their cages and taken away.

Suddenly, a new prince arrived in a chariot. It was Krishna, with Arjuna as his charioteer. Krishna wanted to try his luck in the contest to win Satya.

The king welcomed Krishna and told him about the terms of the contest. He accepted the terms and entered the field. The defeated kings and princes looked on.

The wild bulls were all standing in a row, with their heads raised high, as if celebrating their victory. Then they saw another man walking boldly towards them. They stared at him; he stared at them. For the first time the bulls seemed frightened. Krishna was strong and clever. He knew how to tackle these wild animals. Slowly, he walked around, caught the bulls one by one, and firmly yoked them together.

The kings and princes were surprised. There were loud cheers for Krishna. The drummers, pipers and buglers went into action with exciting loud music. The King of Kosala greeted Krishna. He placed Satya's hand in Krishna's. There was joy on all sides.

Then the thwarted kings and princes raised an uproar. They were shocked that Krishna had won the contest and thus the hand of Satya. They rose up in anger and cried, "Who is this Krishna? Is he not a cowherd? Is he not the one who killed his own uncle? How can kings and princes of noble birth allow one of their girls to be married to a mere cowherd?"

The kings and princes talked and talked, and shouted at the top of their voices. They said it was below their dignity to allow a cowherd to marry Princess Satya. They wanted to fight it out with Krishna.

Krishna and Arjuna were about to leave with Satya, when the challenge came. Krishna walked to the chariot, jumped into it, and sat there with Satya by his side. He then asked Arjuna to deal with the kings and princes who had declared war on him.

Arjuna went to them and pleaded for peace. He said that Krishna had won the princess in an open contest, by fair means. He appealed to them not to create unnecessary trouble. But the princes, in their disappointment and anger, would not listen to Arjuna. They wanted to fight.

"Then get ready," said Arjuna. He took out his mighty

bow Gandivam, and started shooting arrows that fell like a heavy shower on his foes. The princes shot back but they were no match for Arjuna.

Arjuna aimed his arrows in such a way that he did not kill anyone. His arrows hit the bows and arrows of his enemies, who were left without weapons to fight back. Still the princes wanted to continue the battle. Then Arjuna shot arrows which destroyed the clothes worn by his enemies, leaving all the kings and princes quite naked on the battlefield.

In their shame, all the defeated kings and princes ran away.

Krishna then took leave of the King of Kosala and drove away with Satya by his side, and Arjuna as the charioteer.

Syamantakam

Satrajit was a pious man. He was a devotee of Surya, the sun god. He worshipped Surya for a long time. Surya was pleased. He appeared before Satrajit and asked him to name his wish.

Satrajit was a poor man. He wanted to become rich. He asked Surya to help him to get rich.

Surya granted Satrajit's wish. He gave Satrajit a precious stone called Syamantakam. Surya told Satrajit, "This will produce a good quantity of gold every day. Look after it well."

Syamantakam was a bright gem, shining like the sun itself. Satrajit took it home. People who saw it thought that Syamantakam was Surya, the sun god, himself. They feared that something bad might happen because the sun god had appeared on earth. So they went to Lord Krishna for advice.

Krishna talked to them. He tried to calm their fears. Syamantakam, he said, was only a precious stone. There was no cause for anxiety about it. Krishna also told them that Satrajit was bringing the gem for him to see.

Satrajit went to see Krishna and showed him Surya's wonderful gift. "It is bright and wonderful," Krishna told

Satrajit. "It shines like the sun. It can produce gold every day. People will come to know about this gold you get every day. Beware of robbers."

Krishna added, "Perhaps it is risky for you to keep this precious stone. If you like, you can leave it here with me. I shall take care of it. You can come here every day and collect the gold it produces."

Satrajit was unwilling to part with Syamantakam. He thought Krishna was trying to steal it.

"My Lord," he said, "I received this gift after worshipping Surya for many years. I would like to keep it myself. I think even Surya would not like me to give it away. I beg you not to ask for it."

Krishna said, "I do not want the stone. I only wanted to help you to keep it safe. It is your property and you may take it home. You can do whatever you want with it."

Satrajit was happy. He went home. He took very good care of Syamantakam. Every day the bright gem produced a good quantity of gold and Satrajit became richer and richer.

Satrajit had a brother named Prasenan. This young man was very fond of rich clothes and costly jewels. One day, Prasenan was going to hunt in the jungle with a large number of people. He had put on his best clothes and costly jewels. But he thought he would look better if he wore Syamantakam also.

Prasenan went to Satrajit and asked for the precious stone. Satrajit was fond of his brother. He loved him so much that he could not say 'no' to Prasenan's request. Satrajit therefore gave Syamantakam to Prasenan and asked him to take care of it.

Prasenan went hunting, wearing the bright Syaman-

takam. The hunt was exciting. Prasenan chased a wild boar. The chase was long and Prasenan went far away from his companions.

Suddenly a lion jumped at Prasenan.

Prasenan fought the lion single-handed. In the fight Prasenan was killed.

The lion was attracted by the brightness of Syamantakam and carried away the gem.

A huge monkey, passing that way, saw the lion. The monkey was attracted by the glow of Syamantakam.

The monkey, who was very strong, chased the lion. The lion was killed in the fight with the monkey.

The monkey took Syamantakam, went to his home in a huge cave, and gave the gem to his children to play with.

Satrajit waited for his brother's return from the hunt. The people who had gone on the hunt with Prasenan had all come back. They were unable to tell Satrajit what had happened to Prasenan.

Satrajit hoped that Prasenan would soon return. He waited for many days. But there was no news of Prasenan.

Satrajit was sad. He began to suspect Lord Krishna. He remembered that Krishna had wanted Syamantakam and that he had not given it to him. Was it possible that Krishna had killed Prasenan and stolen the precious stone?

Satrajit thought hard. His suspicion of Krishna grew strong. But he was helpless. Krishna was the king. Satrajit could not accuse him of murder or robbery.

Satrajit, however, could not keep his thoughts to himself. He told some of his very close friends what he thought of the disappearance of Prasenan and Syamantakam. He asked these friends to keep it a secret.

But each of these friends of Satrajit had his own very close friends. Each of them told a few people what Satrajit had said. They said Krishna had killed Prasenan and grabbed Syamantakam.

These friends told their friends and the story spread far and wide.

In a few days, everybody in the country was talking about Prasenan and Syamantakam—and Krishna's cruel hand in their disappearance.

Women could talk of nothing else. They wanted their children to be careful.

"Take good care of your ornaments," they told their children. "Krishna may steal them, if he gets a chance."

The children were frightened. They began to run away

from Krishna—though they had always loved him.

One day, Krishna saw some children playing by the roadside. They ran away when they saw him. But Krishna heard what they said as they ran away.

One child cried, "Run, run! Run away from Krishna. He is a thief. He will even kill children, to grab their ornaments. That is what my mother said."

The other children said that that was what their mothers had told them, too.

Krishna was shocked. He wanted to know the cause of such ugly rumours against him.

Krishna went about in disguise. He moved among the people. The people did not know who he was. He heard the ugly rumours about him that had spread all over the country. Everybody seemed to believe that Krishna had killed Prasenan and grabbed Syamantakam.

Krishna had to prove that he was innocent. To do that, he had to find Syamantakam. He also had to find out how Prasenan had died.

He called together a few of his friends and set out in search of Syamantakam.

Krishna and his companions went to the jungle where Prasenan had gone for the hunt. After a long search, they found the dead body of Prasenan. But they could not find the precious Syamantakam.

They continued the search. Soon, they discovered the body of a dead lion. They also noticed some footprints leading away from the lion.

Krishna and his party traced these footprints to the mouth of an enormous cave. The footprints led into the cave.

Krishna asked his companions to wait.

It was a wonderful place. There was a long passage. On the walls, on both sides, were beautiful paintings—scenes from the 'Ramayana'. Krishna was surprised. He followed the story in pictures as he walked along the passage. The story ended when he entered a big hall.

Some children were playing in the big hall. They were playing with a brilliant gem. Krishna knew at once that it was Syamantakam.

The children were frightened at the sight of a stranger. They cried out for help.

Suddenly, Krishna heard a thunderous roar. He saw a huge monkey rushing to attack him. There was no time to explain why he was there. The huge monkey jumped at Krishna. There was nothing Krishna could do, except defend himself.

It was a terrible fight. The monkey lashed at Krishna, and Krishna fought back. The fight lasted a long time.

Now, this huge monkey was Jambavan, one of the heroes of the 'Ramayana'. He had grown very old and had retired. With his many children and grandchildren, Jambavan was living happily in that beautiful cave.

Nobody had disturbed him there. Now, a stranger had come and frightened his children. Jambavan did not like it. He wanted to turn out the stranger.

Jambavan fought Krishna, and Krishna fought back. Neither of them would yield to the other. The terrific force of the battle shook the entire jungle.

Krishna had not gone there to fight. He did not wish to fight Jambavan, the veteran 'Ramayana' hero. Krishna wanted to stop the fighting somehow. So he rushed forward, caught hold of Jambavan, and threw him aside with great force.

Jambavan was surprised. Nobody had ever defeated him. He looked at the man who had thrown him down. Then he saw Krishna in the form of Lord Vishnu. And within that form he saw the image of his old master, Rama.

Jambavan was sad that he had fought his own master. He fell at the feet of Krishna and asked for forgiveness. Krishna embraced Jambavan and said, "It was our bad luck that we had to fight each other. But I am happy to meet you, and to see you as strong as ever."

Jambavan shed tears of joy.

Then they sat down to talk. Krishna told Jambavan why he had come to the jungle and how he had come to the cave.

"My Lord," said Jambavan, "the precious stone you are looking for is here; I saw a lion with it and I took it from him. I gave it to the children to play with."

Jambavan went in and brought Syamantakam. He gave it to Krishna.

Everybody was happy. Jambavan's children and grand-children came out and asked Krishna for his blessings.

After some time, Krishna took leave of Jambavan. Out-side the cave, he joined his companions and went straight to Satrajit's home.

Satrajit was happy when he got back the precious Syamantakam. He fell at Krishna's feet. He told Krishna how sorry he was for his evil thoughts and the ugly rumours. Satrajit begged for Krishna's forgiveness. He offered Symantakam to Krishna as a gift.

But Krishna did not want the precious stone. He was glad that he had proved his innocence. He was happy that he had won back the love and trust of the people, young and old.

Gayan

One day an attendant of Indra, whose name was Gayan, was riding fast through the city of Dwaraka. Lord Krishna was returning home after bathing, when Gayan's horse ran so close to him that dirt and mud from the horse's hoofs splashed Krishna from head to foot. Krishna was very angry. He shouted to Gayan to stop. Gayan stopped. "You have committed a crime in riding through the city and you have committed another crime by throwing dirt all over the king of the country. You deserve the most severe punishment. I have decided to kill you for what you have done." So saying, Krishna went into the palace.

Gayan mounted his horse and rode off as fast as he could before Krishna came out again. He knew how powerful Krishna was. He was sure that Krishna would carry out the punishment. However, he decided to seek the help of the gods and ask them to save his life.

He first went to Lord Indra. Indra said that he could not do anything against Lord Krishna, and asked Gayan to go to Krishna himself and pray for forgiveness.

Gayan next went to see Lord Shiva. Shiva was also unwilling to help him. He, too, advised Gayan to go to Krishna and seek his mercy.

Gayan was on his way back from Lord Shiva when he met Narada. Gayan told Narada of Lord Krishna's threat and sought his advice. Narada was always ready with advice if that led to people quarrelling. He thought for a while and said, "I think I shall be able to advise you. There is only one man who can save you and that is Arjuna. Go to Arjuna quickly and seek his help. He will certainly help you. The Pandavas are now in the jungle. Run there before Krishna catches you."

Gayan started off, but Narada stopped him and said, "You must first take a promise from Arjuna that he will protect you, before you tell him of Lord Krishna." Gayan agreed to do so and went on his way to Arjuna.

Gayan went to the jungle camp of the Pandavas. He met Arjuna and fell at his feet. Arjuna raised him from the

ground and asked him what he wanted.

"O Arjuna," Gayan said, "I have come all the way to you to save my life. Somebody has taken a vow a kill me. He is following me and may be here any moment. I have nobody but you to protect me."

"Who is this somebody? Who wants to kill you?" asked Arjuna.

"I cannot mention his name unless you promise that you will save my life," Gayan replied.

Arjuna did not know what to do. His brother, Dharma-putra, said, "It is the duty of a prince to protect a man who seeks help in saving his life." Arjuna took his brother's advice and said, "Whoever may be your enemy, it will be my duty to protect you from him."

Gayan was happy and said calmly, "It is Lord Krishna who wants to kill me. Save me from Krishna."

The Pandavas had one of the greatest shocks of their lives. Lord Krishna was their friend, their guide, and their saviour. How could they ever think of taking a stand against Krishna? But Arjuna had given his word of honour. He had done so without thinking that anybody would approach him for help against Krishna. The Pandavas were in a great difficulty. What could they do to honour their promise and at the same time not offend Krishna?

Bhima said, "Why not tie up Gayan and offer him to Krishna as a gift? Krishna might take pity and spare his life." But this did not appeal to Dharmaputra who thought that Arjuna had to keep his promise. Then, to the great relief of the Pandavas, Narada appeared there. The Pandavas received him with great respect. They told him of their difficulties, and sought his advice.

"Your first duty," said Narada, "is to protect Gayan. It is true that Krishna may not like it. There will even be a fight between Krishna and Arjuna on this account. But I can assure you that none of the Pandavas will ever be killed by Krishna, and he will never be harmed by the Pandavas."

So the Pandavas decided that Arjuna should fulfil his promise and protect the life of Gayan.

Narada then went to Lord Krishna. Krishna was setting out in search of Gayan. "There is no need to look for Gayan," said Narada. "I saw him just now in the camp of the Pandavas. The Pandavas have given him protection and Arjuna is even ready to fight you if need be."

Krishna was astonished. He could not believe that the

Pandavas would at any time stand against him as they were now doing. Still he could not think of a fight between him and the Pandavas. To avoid it he must find some way out.

He called his sister, Subhadra, and said, "Your husband, Arjuna, has taken Gayan into his protection. Gayan has offended me, so I have decided to kill him. You had better go to Arjuna and ask him to surrender Gayan. Tell him that if he does not do so I am going to take Gayan by force. If there is a fight between Arjuna and me, one of us may be killed. If you wish both of us to live, go and ask Arjuna to give up Gayan."

Subhadra was shocked. She did not want a fight between her brother and her husband, at any cost. She had to do something to prevent such a fight and do it quickly.

Subhadra went to the camp of the Pandavas and met Arjuna. She wept and pleaded with him to surrender Gayan to Krishna and said, "We cannot afford to displease Krishna."

Arjuna replied, "O Devi, I do not want to displease Lord Krishna in any way, but I have to do my duty as a prince. I gave my word to Gayan that I would protect him, without knowing that Krishna wanted to punish him. It is my misfortune that in doing my duty I may have to stand against Krishna."

Subhadra had failed in her efforts. She returned to

Krishna and told him what Arjuna had said. Krishna was disappointed. He said to Subhadra, "I am afraid that I cannot settle the matter peacefully. It is God's will that I must fight Arjuna."

Lord Krishna decided to secure Gayan at any cost. He went to the camp of the Pandavas with a large army. He invited Arjuna to meet him and settle the matter peacefully. He told Arjuna of Gayan's offence and of his decision to punish him and said that it would be better for everybody if Gayan were surrendered.

"My Lord, Krishna," said Arjuna, "God is my witness. I have no desire to displease you in any way. I had no reason to believe that you were trying to punish Gayan for an offence he had committed. So I gave him my word that

I would protect him and I have to fulfil my promise."

"Stop all this big talk," shouted Krishna. "Surrender Gayan or be ready for a battle."

"I am not the man to be afraid of any battle," said Arjuna. "If you force me I am ready to meet you in battle."

Lord Krishna began the fight by shooting an arrow. Arjuna stopped it before it reached him. Krishna sent another one which was also stopped by Arjuna. Then Krishna sent another one, and another, but Arjuna defended himself so well that not one of the arrows could touch his body. Krishna ordered a regular battle. A big fight started between the forces of Lord Krishna and those of the Pandavas. The fight developed into a fierce war. The sky and the earth began to tremble. Krishna brought out more and more powerful weapons, and Arjuna defended himself with still more powerful ones. The battle raged for a long time. There was no victory or defeat on either side. Lord Krishna lost patience. He started using the most powerful weapons. But Arjuna had equally powerful ones. At last Krishna was so angry that he took out 'Sudarshan-chakra', the most deadly weapon of all, to use it against Arjuna. But Arjuna was ready with 'Pasupatastra', an equally deadly one. These were weapons which could destroy the world if they were used. The people on earth and the gods in heaven thought that the end of the world was coming. People prayed to the gods to save them from the coming danger. All the gods ran to the battlefield and prayed to Lord Krishna not to use the deadly weapon, and they promised to settle the quarrel. Both Krishna and Arjuna put back their weapons to hear what the gods had to say.

Brahma, the Creator, came forward to make peace. He asked Arjuna to surrender Gayan to him. When Arjuna did so, Brahma handed over Gayan to Krishna. Krishna killed Gayan by cutting off his head. Brahma at once joined the head to the body again and revived Gayan. Gayan stood up as if nothing had happened. Thus both Krishna and Arjuna kept the promise they had made.

Kacha and Devayani

The Devas and Asuras were always fighting each other. The Devas were from amongst the gods. The Asuras were demons. The Asuras were powerful, capable of all kinds of wickedness. Some of them were great rulers and mighty kings.

In their fight with the Devas the Asuras had an advantage. They had on their side a great saint and teacher, Sukracharya, who knew the *mantra* or magic formula for bringing dead people back to life. He restored to life many Asuras who were killed in the battles against the Devas.

The Devas did not have anybody who knew that *mantra*. They went to their chief adviser, Brihaspati, and sought his help. But Brihaspati said, "I do not know the science of giving life to the dead. Only Sukracharya knows it. Somebody from your side should go to him and stay with him as his student and learn the secret."

"We have nobody with us to undertake such a difficult task. But we feel that the best choice for it is your own son, Kacha."

Brihaspati thought for a while, then said, "Yes, let Kacha go."

The Devas called Kacha and asked him if he could render them a service. They said, "Go to Sukracharya and be with him as his disciple for as long as is necessary to learn the science of raising the dead. Serve him with all devotion. You may also be friendly with Devayani, his beautiful daughter. That will help you in attaining your objective."

Kacha promised to do his best to fulfil his mission. He took leave of the Devas and went to Sukracharya's hermitage.

The great sage received him with all kindness.

"O great teacher," said Kacha, "I am Kacha, son of Brihaspati. I want to be your student. I am eager to gain knowledge at your feet."

"You are the son of Brihaspati?" asked Sukracharya. "If so, what can I teach you that your father can't? Anyway, you have come to me in search of knowledge. I shall be happy to help you in whatever way I can."

"I shall be at your service from now on," said Kacha.

"You need not do any heavy work here," said Sukracharya. "You can help me in my prayers by bringing flowers from the jungle. You can also bring firewood for my sacrificial fire and you can look after my cows, take them out for grazing and bring them back in the evening."

"I shall try to do everything to your satisfaction," said Kacha.

Thus, Kacha began to live with Sukracharya. Because of his keen devotion and good service he won the favour of Sukracharya. Kacha was young, handsome, and very intelligent and no wonder Devayani fell in love with him. But Kacha was a student and he could not respond to her love. All the same Kacha liked her and considered her a friend. He gathered flowers and fruits for her and helped

her in her household duties. Sometimes they would wander about the jungles and sometimes they sang and danced together.

In course of time the Asuras found out why Kacha was staying with Sukracharya. They did not want the secret of reviving dead people to be known to the Devas and, therefore, they decided to remove Kacha from Sukracharya's hermitage for good. That could only be done by killing him.

One day when Kacha was taking his master's cows to the jungle the Asuras waylaid him and killed him. But they had to do away with his body. They were afraid that Sukracharya might revive Kacha. So, they cut his body into pieces and gave the pieces to wolves and jackals.

In the evening Devayani waited for Kacha but the cows returned home without him. Devayani was upset. She went to her father and said, "The sun has set, the cows have returned home. Kacha has not come. He is either lost or dead. O father, bring Kacha back. I cannot live without him."

Sukracharya considered for a while as to what could have happened to Kacha. He felt that Kacha was dead and said, "I shall bring him back to life." Then he silently said the secret *mantra* or magic formula.

At once Kacha appeared before the master. When Devayani asked him why he was late, he said, "The Asuras killed me, cut my body into pieces and fed the wolves and jackals with them. When the great saint, your father, summoned me, I came out of the wolves and jackals, tearing their bodies, and now I stand before you."

Kacha continued to live with Sukracharaya and Devayani. But the Asuras did not keep quiet. One day Kacha was in the jungle collecting flowers when the Asuras caught him. They killed him and grinding his body into a paste, they mixed it with the waters of the ocean.

Devayani was again in despair when Kacha did not return from the jungle.

She told her father that she did not wish to live without Kacha. Once again Sukracharya with his magic spell brought Kacha back.

The Asuras were very disappointed at their failures. They thought of a plan to dispose of Kacha in such a way that Sukracharya would never be able to bring him back to life.

The Asuras caught Kacha a third time. They killed him and burnt his body. They collected the ashes and mixed the ashes with the wine that Sukracharya drank.

When Kacha was missing again Devayani said to her father, "Kacha went out to gather firewood but he has not come back. Surely he is lost or dead."

Sukracharya meditated for a while and said, "Yes, Kacha is dead and it is difficult for me to bring him back to life. I am helpless now. Whenever I bring him back to life he is slain again. O Devayani, do not grieve, do not cry. You should not distress yourself for a mortal. Gods are aware of your beauty. Any one of them may propose to you."

But Devayani said, "How can I not grieve for the death of one whom I love? He was handsome. He was great and he was young. No god will be like him. I will starve myself to death and follow him."

Sukracharya was sorry for his daughter and angry with the Asuras who had slain a disciple under his care. At Devayani's request he began summoning Kacha back from death.

Kacha answered in a low voice from his stomach. "I am Kacha," he said. "I was killed by the Asuras, who burnt my body and mixed the ashes with the wine that you have drunk. Be gentle to me, O master. Consider me as your son as I am now part of you."

Then Sukracharya said to Devayani, "What can I do now? Kacha is within me. Either I live or Kacha lives. Both of us cannot exist together hereafter."

"If Kacha dies," said Devayani, "I will not live, and if you die then also I will die."

Sukracharya was in a fix. He said to Kacha, "Victory is yours. Since Devayani looks on you with such kindness, receive from me the magic *mantra*, or the secret of bringing back the dead to life. When you come out of me, try the *mantra* on my body."

Then Sukracharya taught Kacha the secret *mantra* and asked him to come out of his stomach. Kacha appeared in all his brilliance, and saw his teacher lying dead. He immediately revived him with his newly learnt *mantra*.

Kacha then did homage to Sukracharya, calling him father as he was now born out of him.

Kacha stayed with them for some more time and then sought the blessings of his master to return home.

Sukracharya gave Kacha permission to leave but Devayani, seeing him about to depart, said to him, "Don't go away. You know how I have loved you from the time you were a student. Now that you have finished your studies it is time you returned my love and married me."

Kacha said, "I respect you very much. You are dearer than life to me. But you are my sister. Both of us came out of your father. My love for you is a brother's love."

"You are great and I love you," said Devayani. "Remember, my love for you saved you from death thrice. Why did I do that if not for love? Don't discard me. Accept me as your wife."

"It is a sin if I agree to do what you say," said Kacha. "We have spent happy days together as sister and brother. Let us continue that relationship. I can assure you that I cannot be tempted into sinning."

Devayani was so disappointed that she was angry and cursed him. "Since you have betrayed my trust, you will not be able to practise what you have learnt."

Kacha said, "I refused you only because you are my sister. I don't deserve your curse. You have done that in a fit of passion. You said what I have learnt shall be useless, but I shall impart it to someone else and make it useful."

In spite of Devayani's pleadings, Kacha left. He was received by the Devas with great honour.

Banasura

There was once a powerful king whose name was Bana. He was an Asura, or demon. So he was known as Banasura.

Banasura was so strong and fierce that everyone was afraid of him. Even the kings on earth and many gods in heaven feared him.

Banasura was a devotee of Lord Shiva. He once worshipped Shiva with such devotion that Shiva himself appeared before him and said, "I am very pleased with you. I shall grant you whatever you wish for."

Banasura smiled and said, "I am grateful to you for your kind offer. By your grace I have everything I want. I am now a great king. I am so strong that all the other kings and even the gods dare not stand up against me."

"Then you have nothing to wish for," said Shiva.

"I have something to wish for," replied Banasura. "Although I have fought and won many battles, still I fear I may have some enemies. Since you have kindly promised to grant me whatever I wish for, my wish is that you should come with your family and guard the gates of my city."

Shiva was shocked. He was very angry. But he was helpless. He had promised to grant Bana's wish and now he could not withdraw from his promise.

So Lord Shiva, his consort Parvati, and their children all came down to earth and stood guard at the gates of Banasura's city.

Banasura was happy that now the great Shiva himself was serving under him. He informed all the other kings of his remarkable achievement and he invited many to come and see Lord Shiva working as his servant.

One day Banasura went to Lord Shiva and said, "I am tired of my lazy life. I want to have the excitement of war. My hands are itching for a fight. Shall I get the chance to fight somebody who is a match for me?"

"Yes, yes," replied Shiva. "You will certainly get the chance."

"When? When?" asked Bana eagerly. "I want to know when I shall get the chance to fight. I am impatient."

"Keep a watch on your flag on the flag-staff," said Shiva. "When you see the flag-staff broken and the flag fallen down then you will know that the chance for a fight is coming. You will have to fight a great person. He will defeat you and curb your pride."

From that day onwards Banasura kept a close watch on his flag flying on the flag-staff.

Banasura had a beautiful daughter named Usha. She was in the prime of youth and received many proposals of marriage. But her father did not agree to any of them.

Usha had a companion named Chitralekha. She was the daughter of one of Bana's ministers, and the cleverest and most talented woman the world had ever seen. She was very well educated and she was a great artist. She knew everybody who was of any importance in heaven or on earth.

One night Usha dreamt that she was in the company of a very handsome prince. He showed great interest in her and she fell in love with him. Suddenly she woke up and found that the prince was gone.

"Where are you? Come to me," she called loudly but there was no reply.

Then she searched for him in her room and outside. When she could not find him anywhere, she burst into tears.

Chitralekha heard her crying. She went in and asked what had happened. Usha told her that a young and handsome prince had come to her but he had suddenly vanished.

"You must bring him back to me," she said. "If you can't, I have no desire to live."

Chitralekha knew that Usha had only been dreaming. It would be very difficult to find the young man Usha had seen in her dream. However, she promised to try and find him.

Chitralekha thought deeply over the matter. Who could have appeared before Usha? It might be one of the gods, for some of them had played such tricks before. Or perhaps it could be one of the kings. She wrote down the names of all the gods and kings and princes whom Usha might have seen in her dream. She then began to draw portraits of each one in turn.

She began with the gods. She drew Indra and showed the picture to Usha.

"No," said Usha, "that is not the man I saw."

Then Chitralekha drew Brahma, and then many of the Devas. But Usha rejected them all.

Then Chitralekha drew the pictures of kings and princes, but Usha said that none of them resembled her dream lover.

Chitralekha then drew Sri Krishna. Usha said that there was some likeness, but he was not the man.

Then she drew the picture of Krishna's son. Usha said

there was more likeness, but her lover was much younger.

Chitralekha smiled and drew the picture of Anirudha,

Krishna's grandson, who was famous for his beauty, and showed it to Usha.

Usha snatched the picture and said to it, "You, my beloved, why did you go away?"

"He is the man," she said to Chitralekha. And she kept the picture close to her heart.

Chitralekha knew that it was Anirudha with whom Usha had fallen in love. She told Usha who the young man was and explained that it would be a difficult task to get him.

"Nothing is difficult for you," said Usha. "You must get him for me or I shall die."

"Keep calm, Usha," Chitralekha replied. "I promise I shall try my best to find him and bring him to you."

It was midnight when Chitralekha set out on her mission. Unseen by anyone she went to Lord Krishna's palace. She searched from room to room and at last found Anirudha sleeping in his room.

Chitralekha had certain magic powers. She made Anirudha continue to sleep while she lifted him up and put him on her back. She carried him out of the palace and took him away to Bana's city. She went straight to Usha's room. It was dawn when she arrived. She laid Anirudha on Usha's bed.

Usha was very happy to see Anirudha and she kissed Chitralekha in gratitude. Chitralekha left the room saying that she would come back when Anirudha woke up.

Anirudha slept for a long time. Usha gazed at his handsome face. She wanted to wake him up and talk to him. But she was afraid of disturbing him. She gently fanned him.

At last Anirudha opened his eyes and looked around.

He was surprised to find himself in a strange place. He looked at Usha in astonishment. She was very beautiful and he liked her very much. But who was she?

He sat up and said to Usha, "Who are you? Where am I? How did I come here? Have we met before?"

Usha said, "I am Usha, the daughter of King Bana. This is my room. Yes, we have met before. We met in my dream. I fell in love with you and wanted to be with you always. My friend Chitralekha brought you here. Oh, please stay with me!"

Anirudha felt confused. What should he do? Should he stay with Usha or should he return home? Usha was so loving and so lovely that he did not want to leave her. But how could he stay with her? Usha was not married to him. And what would his father and grandfather think when they learnt that he was staying with Bana's daughter?

"What are you thinking?" asked Usha, looking at him eagerly. "Neither my people nor yours will approve of our marriage. But we are made for each other. Please stay with me."

"You are very beautiful," said Anirudha. "I love you very much and I would like to marry you. But it would not be wise to do so without the consent of our parents. Let us consult them first."

"You don't know my father," said Usha. "He will never agree to our marriage."

"But we can argue with him and make him change his mind," said Anirudha.

"I do not know what he will do if he sees you here," said Usha in despair.

Anirudha and Usha were still talking when a maid-servant came in. She saw the handsome stranger in Usha's room. She went and reported the matter to Bana.

Bana at once rushed to his daughter's room. He was shocked to find Usha in the company of a handsome

young man. Bana shouted and roared with anger and fell upon the young man to kill him. Anirudha defended himself bravely.

But Bana was a giant. He overpowered the young prince and was about to kill him when Usha rushed between them and cried, "Father, don't do him any harm. He is my guest. He did not come here by himself. I brought him. He is innocent. He has not done anything wrong. If any wrong has been done, it is I who have done it. He must not be punished for the wrong I did. You can punish me, you can even kill me if you so desire. But don't touch even a hair of my guest, this noble young prince."

Bana was taken aback. Usha had never talked to him so boldly before. He was furious and wanted to kill them both. But he thought for a while and then bound Anirudha's hands and feet, dragged him out and put him in prison.

In the meantime it had been discovered that Anirudha was missing from the palace of Lord Krishna. It was strange that the young prince had suddenly vanished. Nobody had any idea where he had gone. Had he been kidnapped? Or had he met with some disaster? A search was made but the prince could not be found.

Then Narada, the wandering sage, went to Krishna and informed him that his grandson was in Bana's prison. Krishna was surprised. How had Anirudha fallen into the hands of Bana? Bana was an Asura and he would not release Anirudha easily. Krishna knew that the only way to get back his grandson was to wage a war on Bana.

So Krishna gathered a large army and marched to Banasura's capital. In the distance, Krishna saw Bana's flag flying on a tall flag-staff. He shot an arrow. The arrow broke the flag-staff and the flag fell down.

Bana saw the flag-staff broken and the flag fallen down. He knew that the time had come for a fight. He was jubilant. He had been waiting for this for a long time. He assembled his army and marched out to meet the enemy.

He was met outside by the huge army of Krishna. The battle began between the two forces. It was a fierce battle and most of the men in Bana's army were killed. Bana went ahead to face Krishna.

Krishna destroyed Bana's chariot. Bana jumped down and challenged Krishna. He accepted the challenge and then began a terrible fight. Krishna was winning. He was about to kill Bana when suddenly Bana's mother came and stood between her son and Krishna.

"Do not kill my son," she cried. "Kill me first before you harm my son!"

Krishna stopped the fight to talk to her. In the meantime Bana ran and took shelter in the palace.

Shiva was still guarding the gate of the city. Since an enemy had come and attacked Bana, the city was threatened and it was his duty to protect it.

Shiva did not have a large army, so he had to find a new way to overcome the enemy and make them unable to fight. He produced germs of fever and spread them among Krishna's army.

Krishna's soldiers began to develop high fever and started shivering. Soon, one after another, they fell to the ground.

Krishna saw what had happened to his soldiers. He had to do something quickly to save their lives.

He produced germs which would destroy Shiva's germs, and spread them among his soldiers. Soon all his soldiers were quite well again and they stood up, ready to fight.

Then Banasura collected a large army and came out and resumed the battle against Krishna. But Krishna and his men fought fiercely, and soon Bana's army was completely defeated.

Again Krishna and Banasura met in single combat. As Krishna was about to kill Bana, Lord Shiva came forward and asked him to spare Bana's life.

Krishna paid homage to Shiva and then said, "Bana has committed all kinds of crimes. He even cheated you and made you his servant. He does not deserve mercy. But if you want him to live, let him promise to mend his ways."

Bana fell at Krishna's feet and said he was sorry for all he had done. He promised that in future he would be a different man.

Krishna forgave Bana and spared his life.

Bana then turned to Shiva and apologized for the crime he had committed in cheating him and making him serve as his gatekeeper.

Shiva forgave him and said that he was happy that he had been able to protect Bana from Krishna's wrath.

Bana's life was thus saved. Then he went and brought Usha and Anirudha and handed them over to Krishna.

Krishna received them with love. He took them home with him and celebrated their marriage. They all lived happily ever after.

Arjuna and the Kirata

The Pandavas were in exile. They had lost their kingdom and everything they had in a game of dice with their cousins, the Kauravas. The Pandavas were living in jungles and the 12-year period of exile was nearing its end. They began to think of their future. They were not sure that the Kauravas would give them back their kingdom when they returned.

One day a great sage named Vedavyasa came to the forest camp of the Pandavas. He was received with great respect. During their talk with him the Pandavas expressed their fear about their future.

Vedavyasa said, "The Kauravas are now ruling the whole country. They have built up a strong army and they are very powerful. They will not easily give up what they took from you. If you want your kingdom back, you will have to fight the Kauravas for it."

"How can we fight the Kauravas? Where can we raise an army to fight the powerful forces of the Kauravas?" said Dharmaputra, the eldest of the Pandavas.

"It may take you some time to raise an army," said Vedavyasa, "but you have friends and they will help you."

"Kauravas also have their own friends," said Dharma-

putra, "and they will strengthen the Kauravas."

"But you cannot just sit back," said Vedavyasa. "You have to prepare for a war with the Kauravas. I advise you to seek the blessings of Lord Shiva first before you do anything. Let Arjuna go and propitiate the Lord and I am sure he will help you."

The Pandavas accepted Vedavyasa's advice and deputed Arjuna to get the blessings of Lord Shiva.

Arjuna did not know how to do that. He could not go and meet Lord Shiva for he lived far, far above the earth and there were no means to go there. The only way open to Arjuna was to please Lord Shiva by ardent prayers. So Arjuna went into the deep jungle below the great mountain Kailash. He selected a place under a huge tree and started his *tapas*—worship. It was a great task. He had to sacrifice all his comforts and concentrate his thoughts solely on the Lord. In doing so, he gave up food at first, and then water. He stood on one leg for days and days without moving, in meditation.

Birds and animals went near him without fear, thinking that he was something without life. Birds made nests in his hair. Creepers grew by his side and climbed over his body. Snakes crawled about him. Arjuna was not aware of any of these; he was so immersed in his prayers.

God Indra came to know of Arjuna's *tapas*. He wondered why Arjuna had undertaken such a hard task. Was he trying to become one of the gods? Was he aiming to overthrow Lord Indra himself and take his place? Or was he concerned only with defeating the Kauravas? Anyway, Indra was not happy at Arjuna's *tapas*. He wanted to stop him from continuing it. He called the famous courtesans Urvasi, Rambha, Menaka and Tilottama and said, "You are all great beauties, capable of enticing any male, man or god. Arjuna is doing *tapas* in the jungles. I want you to go and draw him away from it. I hope you can."

"Of course," said Urvasi. "Who can withstand our charms? Arjuna will follow us here cringing for favours."

"Good," said Lord Indra, "then go immediately. Take with you a large number of attendants as well."

The celestial courtesans came down to Arjuna with a large number of attendants.

They formed a circle round Arjuna and started dancing and singing. They went round and round, trying their best to attract his attention. But he never even knew that they were there; he was so immersed in meditation.

The four celestial courtesans did all they could but Arjuna could not be seduced. Then they lost their temper. They were angry. They asked their attendants to do their best to divert Arjuna's thoughts. The attendants, most of them ferocious and ugly, tried to frighten Arjuna, but Arjuna was not a man to be frightened. Defeated in their mission, Lord Indra's courtesans and their attendants had to return.

In the meantime, the Kauravas came to know of Arjuna's efforts to please Lord Shiva. They feared that Lord Shiva, when pleased, would provide Arjuna with some powerful weapons which would be used against them. So the Kauravas also wanted to prevent Arjuna from continuing his *tapas*. They sought the help of Mukasura, a terrible demon. He was only too willing to help the Kauravas.

Mukasura went to the jungle as a huge boar. He charged at Arjuna with the intention of killing him. Just then, from somewhere, a great hunter, Kirata, and his wife appeared and the hunter shot an arrow at the wild boar.

In the meantime Arjuna sensed danger from some wild

animal, took his bow and arrow and shot an arrow with such strength that the wild boar was killed immediately.

The hunter's arrow just missed the animal, and fell at Arjuna's feet. Arjuna saw it and thought it was his own arrow which had returned to him after killing the wild boar. So he took possession of the arrow.

Suddenly the hunter and his wife appeared before Arjuna. The hunter demanded his arrow back. Arjuna said that it was his own.

"You are a thief. You have taken something that is not yours," said the hunter.

"No, it is my own arrow that has come back to me after killing the wild boar," said Arjuna.

"Will you give me back my arrow or not?" shouted the hunter.

"No," roared Arjuna.

"If you don't give me back my arrow, I am going to take it from you by force," said the hunter, taking out his bow and arrow and aiming at Arjuna.

"A mere hunter trying to challenge me!" exclaimed Arjuna.

"Yes, you are going to get it hot from a mere hunter," retorted the hunter.

Arjuna got very angry and started shooting arrows like rain at the hunter. The hunter's wife was frightened but by her miraculous powers she turned all the arrows shot by Arjuna into flowers. Soon a mountain of flowers covered the hunter.

Arjuna then challenged the hunter to come out and fight. The hunter accepted the challenge and there was a great hand-to-hand fight between the hunter and Arjuna. Arjuna felt he was losing and the hunter started taunting him for his inability to win against a 'mere hunter'. He caught Arjuna with his powerful hands and threw him down with such force that he lay helpless on the ground. He wondered how he could be beaten. He prayed to Lord Shiva and again sought his blessings. He wanted to know from the Lord why he was defeated by a hunter. He made an idol of Lord Shiva out of mud and worshipped it with all devotion. He closed his eyes and said his prayers. Suddenly he felt that some new power had come to the idol. He opened his eyes and saw Lord Shiva and Parvati standing before him.

Lord Shiva raised Arjuna from the ground and said that

he was very pleased to meet one of the greatest heroes of the world.

"My Lord," said Arjuna, "I am not at all a hero. A mere hunter just defeated me in a fight."

Lord Shiva smiled and said, "I wanted to try your strength. It was I who took the form of a hunter and challenged you. Now I am convinced of your great strength. You will always win in any fight. Here is something which will help you."

Lord Shiva then handed over to Arjuna 'Pasupatastra' , the greatest weapon ever seen anywhere, and blessed Arjuna and wished him all success.

Vishvamitra

Vishvamitra is generally known as a great saint. But before he became a saint he was a great king. He ruled over a vast kingdom. He was very powerful. He waged wars against rival rulers and won all of them.

Vishvamitra was very fond of hunting. One day he went into the jungles with a large number of attendants. He spent an exciting day hunting various kinds of animals. By evening the king and his companions were very tired. They started their journey back. They were hungry and thirsty. They longed to have some water and food. On their way they saw a hermitage. It was a small place and the king was not sure if they could get even water there. Perhaps, he thought, the sage in the hermitage would show them the way to some pond or river where they could quench their thirst. The king went to meet the sage.

The sage was the great Vasishta, one of the greatest saints and teachers of the world. But to the king he looked an ordinary sage. Even so, the king requested him for help to find water for his party.

"You must all be hungry too," said the sage. "I shall try to help you."

Soon Vasishta produced a large quantity of milk, enough

for the king and his companions. He also produced the most delicious food that Vishvamitra and party had ever tasted. "Amazing," said the king to his friends. "How could the sage produce all this in such a short time? And without any preparations." He could not see any other human being. There was only a cow and her calf at the hermitage.

Night had already set in when the hunting party finished their meal. Vasishta said, "Your Majesty, you must be very tired. I think you should all rest before you start for your capital."

Vishvamitra's curiosity was further aroused. Having given them plenty of milk and food, did Vasishta now plan to provide sleeping facilities for all of them? How? he asked himself. He could not see any place to sleep and he did not like to embarrass his kind host. So he thanked the saint for all his kindness and said that he would like to continue his journey with his people.

"Please don't worry," said Vasishta, "I have enough cots and bedding for all of you." This was interesting, thought Vishvamitra. How and from where would Vasishta get those things. But in a few minutes Vasishta produced the most comfortable beds for Vishvamitra and his men. Being tired, the king and his party gave no more thought to this miracle and spent the night in sound sleep.

Early next morning everybody was given fresh milk. Vishvamitra could not hold his curiosity any longer.

"May I ask you a question?" asked Vishvamitra.

"Yes, yes, any number of questions," replied Vasishta.

"How did you produce all these luxurious things in a lonely place like this? I find no other human being except you. How could you do all these miracles?"

"Not much of a miracle," said Vasishta. "Look at that cow. Is there anything strange about her?"

"She is a beautiful cow," said Vishvamitra. "I was admiring her from the moment I saw her and her lovely calf."

"Well," said Vasishta, "she is not an ordinary cow. She is a wonderful cow. She is Nandini, daughter of Kamadhenu. She can give anything you ask of her."

That was really wonderful, Vishvamitra thought, but what was such a cow doing in a hermitage? She ought to be with the king of the land.

"Your Holiness," said the king, "I was wondering why such a cow is kept in a lonely place like this. You are a saint. You don't need Nandini. She should be with the king. Won't you be pleased to give her to me as a gift?"

"She cannot be given away like that," said Vasishta. "She is here to look after my needs."

"I shall give you a thousand cows," said Vishvamitra, "if you will give this cow to me."

"What would I do with your thousand cows?" said Vasishta. "I am not a cowherd to look after a thousand cows."

"Why do you want to keep this cow?" asked Vishvamitra. "She is wasted here. If she is with me the world will benefit from her presence."

"I am sorry, Your Majesty," said the saint. "Nandini remains here and you cannot have her."

"I am being very polite to you," said the king, beginning to get annoyed. "As King Vishvamitra, I demand the cow, but I shall be kind to you. I shall give you, in return, anything you desire."

"I desire nothing," said Vasishta. "I have regard for you as a king but a king cannot have all he wants."

Vishvamitra felt that he was being disobeyed. He was not the one to take any humiliation lying down. He wanted Nandini and he decided to have her.

"Take that cow and follow us," he ordered two of his men. The men untied Nandini and tried to take her along with them. But Nandini had no intention of going with them. King or no king, she was Vasishta's. She broke loose and Vishvamitra's men could not hold her. The men then untied the calf and tried to march it along, hoping the cow would follow. This was too much for Nandini. She became ferocious and charged Vishvamitra's men with such force that they ran for their lives.

Vishvamitra then told Vasishta that he would not be thus insulted. That just then he had to go but he would come back to take Nandini.

Vishvamitra returned to the palace and ordered his army to be ready. Soon he was on his way to Vasishta's hermitage with a large force. But there he had a surprise waiting for him. At the hermitage they were met by a larger army.

A fierce battle was fought. Vishvamitra's forces were completely defeated. The king was puzzled. Even though he had fought against Vasishta, yet he decided to meet him.

The king asked the sage how he was able to win.

Vasishta said, "This is all Nandini's doing. I have already told you that the cow is not an ordinary one. One can have anything from her as long as it is not for oneself. Whenever I ask Nandini for something it is not for myself but for somebody else."

Vishvamitra felt that he was after all not as great as sage Vasishta. The sage commanded greater powers than a king's army or wealth. He decided then and there that he would also attain a position equal to, if not better than, that of Vasishta.

Vishvamitra admitted defeat and left.

"No, Your Majesty, you shall go back with all the soldiers you brought with you."

And lo and behold! All those who had fallen in the battlefield arose as if they had just been asleep.

As a parting shot Vishvamitra said to Vasishta, "I am taking leave of you, great sage, but I am not going to sit idle. I will do everything in my power to attain a position better than yours. And then we shall meet again."

Vishvamitra returned to his palace. He immediately gave up his kingdom and all his wealth and went to the deepest jungle to meditate. It took him many, many years to be an equal of Vasishta and when he attained that position his only ambition was to oppose Vasishta in anything he said and try to defeat him in every possible way.

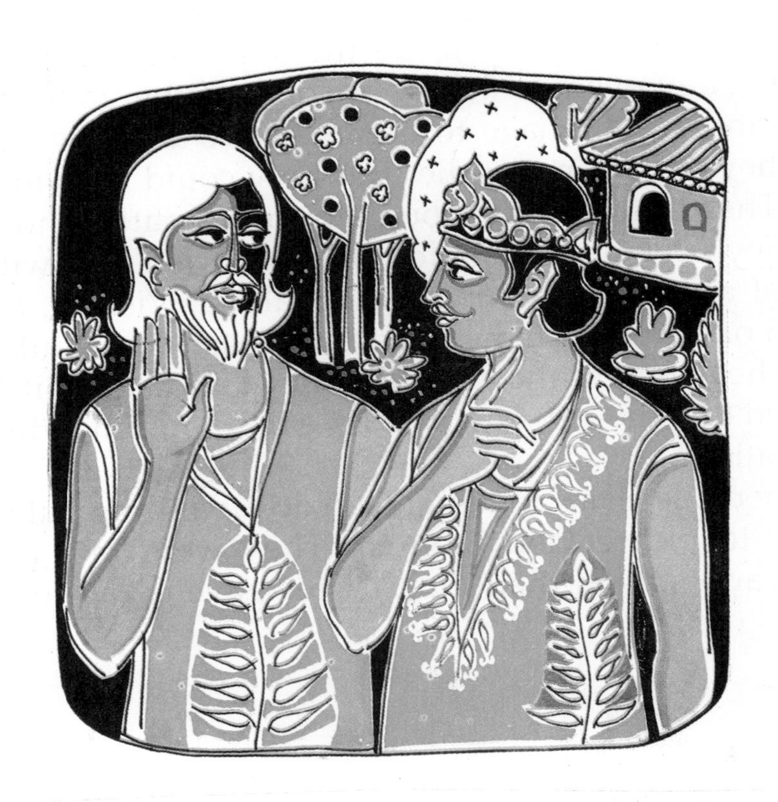

Sundan and Upasundan

Sundan and Upasundan were two Asura princes. They were brothers and looked almost alike. They were very strong and could perform many wonderful feats of strength. It was said that each brother could lift an elephant by the tail, whirl it and throw it miles and miles away.

Sundan and Upasundan loved each other so much that nothing could ever divide them. They were very ambitious too. They wanted to be the supreme rulers of the world. They even wished that some of the gods should come and pay homage to them. Above all, they wanted that they should never die. But how could they manage that? They thought and thought over the matter and in the end they felt that they could fulfil their wish only with the help of a god. But which god? Brahma, Vishnu, Shiva? Which one would be the easiest to please and would give them the blessings they sought. They talked about it. They decided that they would propitiate Lord Brahma, the God of Creation.

They made all arrangements to do *tapas*, or great meditation, to please God Brahma. They went into a thick jungle and started their *tapas*. They gave up all comforts

and remained in deep meditation for months.

Lord Indra was not happy at the *tapas* of the Asura brothers. He feared that they were doing it with the intention of securing great powers from some higher gods, which might enable them to oust him from his kingdom. So Indra wanted to stop the Asura brothers from continuing their *tapas*. He sent his courtesans and their attendants down to the jungle to try their best to disturb the Asuras.

But Sundan and Upasundan were so determined that nothing could sway them from their meditation.

At last God Brahma was moved by the devotion and determination of the Asura brothers. He appeared before them and said, "I am very pleased with your great devotion and love for me. Please tell me in what way I can be of help to you."

"We want a position like that of Lord Indra," the brothers said.

"I am sorry but that is not possible," said Brahma. "Indra is one of the gods and no one can aspire to his position. You can ask for some other favour."

"We are disappointed," said the brothers. "We cannot be satisfied with little things. Our ambition is to conquer the whole world. We have got the strength for that. You can give us one boon—that no god or man will be able to kill us. If at all we die, it shall be only at the hands of each other." The brothers were sure that would never happen. They loved each other so much. They had no fear that there would ever be any difference between them.

"Your wish is granted," said Brahma. "You will not be killed by anybody expect by one another."

The Asura brothers were happy. They returned home and lived in prosperity and happiness. But after sometime they were bored by their peaceful life. They decided to wage war against other princes.

"We must first be the lords of all the world," they said, "and then we must challenge Lord Indra himself. Why should he have all the privileges which he enjoys?"

Soon the Asura brothers started wars against other countries. They won all the wars, killed many kings, destroyed their capitals, looted all their wealth and carried away their beautiful women.

The Asura brothers became the undisputed rulers of the world. There was nobody to question their supremacy. Their word was law. They enjoyed absolute power. Then they planned to cross swords with some of the gods. Lord Indra, who had tried to stop their *tapas*, was their first choice. And they began preparing for an attack on him.

The people of the world and the gods above were greatly worried about the Asura brothers. They were a terror to everybody, but nobody was strong enough to stand up against them.

Many of the gods and saints approached Lord Brahma and complained about the misdeeds of Sundan and Upasundan. Brahma smiled and said, "I am not unaware of the deeds of the Asura brothers. Have a little patience. I shall try to rid the world of this evil."

Lord Brahma thought deeply for a while and then with his powers he created the most beautiful woman ever. He named her Tilottama. She bowed before Brahma and asked, "My Lord, why have you created me? Have I got any special duty to do? I am ready to carry out your orders."

Brahma replied, "Tilottama, you are the most charming woman I have ever created and you can win the hearts of gods and men alike, without much effort. Sundan and

Upasundan are two Asura brothers. They are creating trouble all over the world and even in heaven. I gave them a boon that they would never die at the hands of any man or god. They can be killed only by each other. But there is so much love between the brothers that neither can come to any harm from the other. You are to go to them and create discord between them so that they will quarrel and kill each other."

"Your orders will be carried out," said Tilottama. When she was leaving she saw Lord Indra following her, charmed by her beauty. She told him that she would meet him on her return from her mission.

The Asura brothers were enjoying themselves by playing with hundreds of women in the garden. There was music and dancing. Tilottama appeared suddenly from behind a tree.

"Who is that?" asked Sundan.

"I have not seen her before," said Upasundan.

Tilottama went to the brothers and said, "I am Tilottama. I am touring some parts of the world. I was attracted by the sound of music here, so I just came in to have a look."

"You are most welcome," said the brothers together. "You can stay with us and we will give you whatever you want, money, jewels, costly costumes and hundreds of servants to look after your comforts."

"Give me a little time. Let me think over the matter," said Tilottama.

"What is there to think about?" said Sundan. "I am the elder brother and you shall be my wife."

"Let her decide for herself. Let her see who will be the better one to marry, you or me," said Upasundan.

"Forget about marriage for the present," said Tilottama.

"I am hungry. Let me first have something to eat and then let me join the other ladies in their play."

The Asura brothers ordered food for Tilottama. Hundreds of servants rushed in with various kinds of delicious food. Tilottama started to eat. She looked at the brothers and asked them to join her and they were only too delighted to sit with her and eat. Tilottama was acting her part well. Each brother felt that the celestial beauty liked him better than the other. Each one was waiting for a chance to declare his love for her.

After taking food Tilottama joined the other ladies in dancing and singing and playing various kinds of games. All the while the Asura brothers were trying, separately, to draw her attention. Tilottama too wanted to meet them one by one. Then by chance she met the elder brother, Sundan.

Sundan said, "You are my love. I want to marry you. I shall give you whatever you want."

Tilottama replied, "I like you very much, but your younger brother said that he loves me better."

"Nonsense," said Sundan. "He is a fool, he doesn't know what he says."

"Give me a little time to think over your proposition," said Tilottama, and moved away.

Upasundan now got a chance of meeting her.

"Tilottama, my dear, I love you so much that I want to marry you immediately."

"I think I also like you much," said Tilottama, "but your brother will not like that. In fact, he has proposed to me and I told him about my interest in you. He was rather furious and assured me that he would have you out of the way."

"He said that?" asked Upasundan. "Then tell him that you love me and me alone."

"How can I do that?" said Tilottama. "You are equal in every way and you are both handsome. If I tell him that he may not believe me."

"I shall make him believe you," said Upasundan.

After some more singing and dancing, closely watched by the Asura brothers, Tilottama walked towards the palace, followed by the two.

When they were all in the palace hall Sundan said to his brother, "I am happy to tell you, brother, that I am going to marry Tilottama."

"Nonsense," said Upasundan. "I am going to marry her and I have already asked her to marry me."

"What right have you to ask her?" shouted Sundan. "I am your elder brother and you are to take orders from me."

"We are brothers and we are equal," said Upasundan. "I am not going to give up Tilottama even for the sake of my brother."

"You better think again. I have decided to marry her," said Sundan.

"As long as I am alive, I will not allow anybody else to touch her. She is mine and I am hers."

"Then, listen," said Sundan. "I shall kill anybody who claims her. She is mine and I am hers."

"I am strong enough to stop anybody from coming between me and Tilottama," said the younger brother.

"I am strong enough to destroy whoever comes between me and my love," retorted Sundan.

"Stop bragging," shouted the younger brother. "I will have to kill you for the sake of my love."

"I will break your head if you say that you want Tilottama," said the elder brother.

"Then let us see who wins her," said the younger brother.

And both were ready for a fight.

"Do you want to fight for my sake?" said Tilottama. "It is true that you are nice princes, but I cannot marry both of you. I would have liked to marry one of you, but you are quarrelling. I better go back to Lord Indra, who told me

once that he loved me. But I did not like him much then."

"Please don't go to Indra, marry me," said both the brothers at the same time.

"Will you stop that silly talk?" asked each brother of the other.

"You shut up," said Sundan.

"Then I shall make you shut up," shouted Upasundan.

Angry words then led to a fight between them.

The fight was so fierce that it did not last long.

The brothers killed each other.

Tilottama had fulfilled her mission. She returned to Lord Brahma and told him of her success.

"I knew you could do that," said Brahma, "and now Lord Indra is here to take you to his court. All good wishes to you."

King Shibi

King Shibi was a great ruler. Everything he did was right and noble. He was very kind-hearted. He loved his subjects like his children. He loved animals too and looked after their welfare. He was very charitable and no needy man went away from him without help. He protected the weak against the strong. If anybody sought asylum with him, he shielded him with all his might. His fame as the greatest king spread far and wide. Even gods were getting a little jealous of King Shibi.

One day when King Shibi was holding court, a dove flew in. He was in great fear and took shelter in the king's lap. The dove cried, "O king, protect me from my enemy. He is following me to kill me."

The king said, "Shed your fears, dear bird, for none need fear who seek refuge here."

Then a huge hawk who was chasing the dove, arrived. He had heard the king's assurance to the dove. "This bird is my food," said the hawk. "You should not protect my lawful prey. I have won it after hard labour. O king, I am hungry. You must not prevent me from eating my food. You have no right to take away what belongs to me. You may interfere in the case of human beings but birds are

free in the sky. You have no right to interfere. Please surrender the dove before I die of hunger."

"If you are hungry," said the king, "I shall arrange for the meat of a bull or boar or deer to be given to you. That will be better than the flesh of this small dove."

"I do not eat the flesh of bulls, boars or deer. Doves are my natural food and I must have the food I like," the hawk replied.

"But there must be some other food you like. If so, just say what that is. I shall get that. Please let this bird go."

"If you have so much love for this dove," said the hawk, "give me flesh from your body equal in weight to that of the dove."

"Great is your kindness. What you say shall be done." So saying King Shibi ordered a pair of scales and a sharp knife to be brought to him. He put the dove on one side of the scale and started cutting his own flesh to weigh it against the dove. When they saw what the king was doing, the queen, the ministers and servants were in great distress. But the king told them to be calm. He was only doing his duty.

Then a strange thing happened. The king cut pieces of flesh from his arms and thighs, filling the scale, but the bird always weighed heavier. More and more flesh from the king's body was added, still the bird was heavier. The king was surprised and finally he himself stepped onto the scale and the scale balanced. He asked the hawk to eat him up. But lo! There was no hawk and immediately the dove also disappeared.

In their place appeared God Indra and God Agni (God of Fire). They made the king's body whole.

The gods told King Shibi who they were and that they

just wanted to test him. One of them had taken the form of the hawk and the other that of the dove. They said, "You are great and generous and your name shall be remembered as long as the world lasts."

The king bowed low and thanked them. After blessing the king again, the divine beings left for their heavenly abode.